# Program Cookbook

130 Essential Recipes
+ Easy Tips and Tricks

**Vice President, Content:** Stacey C. Rivera

**Global Creative Director:** Theron Long

**Executive Managing Editor:** Amy Grippo

**Senior Director of Content Innovation:** Jill Herzig

**Food Editor:** Eileen Runyan

**Writer and Project Editor:** Alice K. Thompson

**Contributing Editors/Writers:** Jackie Mills, MS, RD; Deborah Mintcheff; Ann Taylor Pittman

**Nutrition Consultant:** Laureen Jean Leyden

**Recipe Developers:** Terry Grieco Kenny, Frank Melodia, Angela Nilsen, Carol Prager

**Art Director:** Ed Melnitsky

**Designers:** Rebecca Kollmer, Lan Yin Bachelis

**Production Manager:** Alan Biederman

**Photo Director:** Marybeth Dulany

**Photographer:** David Malosh

**Food Stylist:** Simon Andrews

**Prop Stylist:** Suzie Myers



Printed in the USA

**ABOUT WW**

**WW** (formerly Weight Watchers) is a global wellness company and the world's leading commercial weight-management program. We inspire millions of people to adopt healthy habits for real life. Through our engaging digital experience and face-to-face group workshops, members follow our livable and sustainable program that encompasses healthy eating, physical activity, and a helpful mindset. With more than five decades of experience in building communities and our deep expertise in behavioral science, we aim to deliver wellness for all. To learn more about the WW approach to healthy living, please visit WW.com. For more information about our global business, visit our corporate website at corporate.ww.com.

Turkey meatball and escarole soup, page 46

Spelt spaghetti with broccoli rabe, page 132

# Contents

# Eat *your* way

Welcome to a new blueprint for wellness. Good food—and the joy of sharing it with friends and family—is something we at WW are passionate about. Our goal in this book is to inspire and empower you to cook healthy meals for yourself and those you love throughout your weight-loss journey and beyond. Making a good meal is an expression of self-care, after all, and an act of love when it extends outward to your family and friends.

WW is more flexible and livable than ever because it takes your personal needs into account, and *The myWW™ Program Cookbook* focuses specifically on aligning your WW experience with your lifestyle and goals. In the following pages, we share super-simple solutions for breakfast, lunch, and dinner, plus give you the tips to help you throw together great snacks and desserts. And of course we've brought you a trove of delicious recipes that make healthy eating doable in your busy life. Many are designed to be on the table in 30 (or even 20!) minutes or less, while others are ideal for leisurely, celebratory meals—because life has room for both.

We've chosen the recipes, techniques, and tips throughout this book to support you, whether you're an avid cook ready for new adventures or a newbie who wouldn't mind some hand-holding in the kitchen.

Throughout this book we've put an emphasis on well-being as well as weight loss. As always, no foods are off-limits, and we've prioritized the joys of eating and sharing meals with those closest to you. Here's to a delicious journey—and a happier, healthier you.

Enjoy!

**Brown rice and veggie collard wraps, page 70**

# Lose weight, your way

Instead of following someone else's definition of healthy, WW gives you the opportunity to discover your own.

WW is the world's top science-based plan for weight loss, but the program is not just about the numbers on the scale. Our approach emphasizes balance—not only in what you eat. It's a new direction for everyday living, built around joy, connection, and the power of healthy habits. Here's how:

### You'll eat what you love.

Everything is on the menu! The WW program gives you the freedom to make choices that work. You'll eat well, discover fresh tastes, and feel good about your new eating habits.

### You'll find what moves you.

Activity comes naturally when you enjoy what you're doing. Maybe you're already committed to a sport or exercise routine, or perhaps the WW community will help you find a new approach. Either way, the goal is to feel stronger, more powerful, and proud of what your body can do.

### You'll shift your mindset.

WW emphasizes thinking in new ways and confronting tough moments with self-compassion. And since WW is a community-based program, you can turn to your fellow members for support and encouragement in real life and online.

### You'll benefit from the power of SmartPoints®.

Science-backed and easy to use, the SmartPoints system guides you to a healthier pattern of eating. Members learn the specifics about how to calculate SmartPoints from their WW Coaches, but here are some basics:

- Every food and drink has a SmartPoints value based on calories, saturated fat, sugar, and protein.
- You get a daily SmartPoints Budget to spend on any food or drink you like.
- You'll keep track of your SmartPoints in the WW app.
- Are your weekends different from the rest of your week? Up to 4 daily SmartPoints that you don't use will roll over into your weeklies.

### For more flexibility, you have ZeroPoint™ foods.

There are many items that you don't have to track or measure. Why? It's because they form the foundation of a healthy eating pattern, and you have a low risk of overeating them.

## How this book can help you every day

**1**

To help you plan your meals more easily, we've divided the recipes into chapters on breakfast, lunch, dinner, desserts, and snacks. We also start every chapter with a Recipe Builder; this handy visual guide gives you kitchen confidence and a starter set of skills to get going. Then you can begin to improvise, swap ingredients, experiment, and have fun.

**2**

Every recipe includes SmartPoints values for all three WW plans, so it's easy to choose the meals that fit best with your SmartPoints Budget. You can also turn to the "Recipes by SmartPoints® value" index on page 191 at the back of the book; here you can see at a glance what works best for you—you'll even find recipes with just 1 or 2 SmartPoints per serving.

**3**

Need some inspiration? Check out "Meal planning that works" on page xiv. You'll find ideas for cooking ahead, smart shopping, and packing great lunches to take on the road. We've included a rundown of equipment that makes cooking easy, plus a guide to using spices that proves even the simplest meal never, ever has to taste like diet food.

**4**

Finally, we've included expert tips and easy hacks throughout the recipe pages of the book. These will help you get the most out of each recipe, whether they offer advice on how to best make it fit into your personal eating plan, instructions for how to make it ahead, or tips for where to shop for the best and freshest ingredients.

# The new basics

With a little time spent planning, cooking healthy meals at home can become second nature. We're here to make it easier and more enjoyable. These answers to common questions should help you on your way.

## What makes a meal or a recipe "healthier"?

Certainly the ingredients that go into it are a big part: A variety of fruits and vegetables, lower-sugar carbs, lean proteins, and healthy fats. Emphasizing these foods is the basis for the recipes in this book.

- Most fruits and vegetables are ZeroPoint foods on the WW program, so we include them liberally (and deliciously!) in recipes.
- Many lean proteins are also either ZeroPoint foods or low in SmartPoints. To reduce the fat in your meals, trim foods of excess fat and remove skin when appropriate.
- Finally, eating right-for-you portions is key to weight loss. Our recipes give you exact serving sizes and SmartPoints, making it easy to track and learn what works for you.

## Are some techniques better for healthy cooking?

Just as all foods are on the menu, WW also embraces all cooking techniques. There are no "not ok" ways to prep meals and snacks. That said, your daily cooking could be healthier, with some tried-and-true techniques that maximize flavor:

- Our recipes often turn to roasting, searing, and grilling to develop deep, caramelized flavor naturally, without using a lot of oil.
- Stir-frying, steaming, and braising are great for at locking moisture into foods while keeping the added fat down. The Instant Pot® makes short work of some of these methods, so we use it frequently.
- Firing up the broiler or using an air fryer can give food a fantastic crunchiness that rivals deep frying—without added fat.

## What swaps make foods tastier and healthier?

Cutting back on added fats, added sugar, and added salt can have a big impact on your health in the long run. And in the short run? Cutting back on two out of three of those—sources of fats and sugar—can stretch your SmartPoints Budget. Here are places to start:

- Swap in creamy foods like Greek yogurt, silken tofu, and low-fat buttermilk for all or part of higher-fat ingredients like cream, butter, mayonnaise, and sour cream.
- Lower the amount of oil you need to keep foods from sticking by using nonstick pans for searing and lining roasting pans with parchment paper.
- Go for herbs and spices before you immediately season your food with lots of salt. See "Season strategically" on page xxii for fantastic spice blends.

## Easy ways to eat more plants

**If you're trying to eat more plant-based foods—for your health and the health of the planet—WW is here to help, with thousands of easy, tasty recipes. And your ingredient options go way beyond ZeroPoint fruits and veggies. All these are plant-based, too:**

### Beans and lentils

**Protein-rich, fiber-packed legumes can be the main event themselves in dishes from soups and stews to tacos, or they can boost other ingredients in dishes like chili, salads, pasta, and more. You can keep a few cans around so you always have a stash, or cook up a big pot and freeze what you won't eat in a few days. See page xxvii for our Beans from scratch recipe.**

### Grains

**Whole grains like brown rice, quinoa, farro, freekeh, barley, corn, and oats are fantastic sources of fiber and other nutrients, including many of the same antioxidants widely touted in fruits and vegetables. Go beyond just plunking a scoop down as a side dish: Add grains to salads, burger mixes, or your morning breakfast bowl; try whole-grain pastas; and pop up a batch of popcorn for snacks (see Recipe Builder, page 166).**

### Meat and dairy substitutes

**Wider interest in plant-based diets has made meat and dairy substitutes tastier and more varied. New burger patties and sausages that mimic beef and pork are enticing meat lovers, and a host of nondairy cheeses and beverages are fun to explore.**

# What's your plan?

When it comes to losing weight and getting healthier, WW knows that what works for one person might not work for another. The answer? Three science-backed, proven plans that are tailored to fit individual needs and personal preferences.

We've developed every recipe in this book to work for all plans, and we've given the SmartPoints® values up front for each. You can also check out our "Recipes by SmartPoints® value" on page 191 at the back of the book; this gives you an instant overview of how different dishes stack up on different plans.

## Top tips for smarter tracking

Use these proven tips to make tracking simpler:

### 1
### Pre-track when you can

Before each day starts, think about where you're likely to be and pre-track your food and drinks. This will create a mini meal plan for you, giving you confidence that your choices will fall within your Budget. It also helps you to make faster (and better) decisions when you're eating out.

### 2
### Create a backup

It can be hard to remember what you've eaten by the end of the day. That's why it's best to track as you go. But if you find yourself in a bind, put your phone to work: Take a photograph of what you're eating so you can track it later in the day.

### 3
### Repeat your successes

Had a successful week of tracking and reaching your goals? Use it as a guide for upcoming weeks.

Green guides you toward a smaller list of foods that form the basis of healthy eating habits, with a sizable SmartPoints® Budget to spend on other foods you love. You'll build meals and snacks around 100+ ZeroPoint™ foods including fruits and veggies, and track other foods that have SmartPoints values.

Blue guides you toward a list of foods that form the basis of healthy eating habits, with a moderate SmartPoints Budget that you can spend on other foods you love. You'll build meals around 200+ ZeroPoint foods including fruits, veggies, and lean proteins, and track other foods that have SmartPoints values.

Purple guides you toward a long list of foods that form the basis of healthy eating habits, with a modest SmartPoints Budget that you can spend on other foods you love. You'll build meals around 300+ ZeroPoint foods including fruits, veggies, lean proteins, and whole grains, and track other foods that have SmartPoints values.

Orange–cream cheese cookie cups, page 155

# Meal planning that works

## Weekend warrior: 10 ways to make healthy meals a reality

A few hours on the weekend, or whenever it's convenient for you, can make weekday meals smoother and more efficient. Everyone's schedule and lifestyle is different, so pick and choose strategies that work best for your household.

**1 Look at your calendar for the upcoming week.** Getting an idea of how many meals you'd like to cook at home, how many lunches you (or your family) might want to tote to work or school, and how busy you'll be is an ideal way to start planning.

**2 Prepare some meal components.** A big batch of grains, a pot of beans, or a couple quarts of homemade marinara can live in your fridge or freezer and streamline your weeknight cooking. See our section "8 must-have recipes" on page xxiv for some of the DIY staples you can turn to.

**3 Plan for leftovers.** Do weekends mean you have time for simmering a stew, roasting a whole chicken, or assembling your favorite casserole? Think of doubling these recipes or making enough so that you have at least one go-to meal for later in the week. Freezing is great for soups, stews, and casseroles. Roasts like chicken or pork will keep for about three days in the fridge, and you can use them in everything from salads to sandwiches to tacos.

**4 Assemble an emergency dinner kit.** Don't be caught off guard: Stock a corner of your pantry with ingredients you can throw together for a healthy meal on the fly. Ideas? Some dry spaghetti, a can of chickpeas, and a can of water-packed tuna can make a delicious Mediterranean pasta dish with just the addition of garlic, olive oil, and maybe a fresh herb (if you have one!). Store all the elements in a kitchen basket for easy retrieval.

**5 Make some spice blends.** A plain roasted chicken breast, a grilled fish fillet, or even baked tofu can make stellar dinner centerpieces with a simple seasoning blend or rub. Check out our "Season strategically" spread on page xxii for a rundown of five international standouts you can mix up quickly on the weekend.

**6 Plan for your slow cooker or Instant Pot®.** These appliances make dinner easier to prepare, so make sure you have the fixings on hand to load them up on your busiest weekdays.

**7 Think about breakfasts.** Imagine your ideal morning start, whether it's a comforting bowl of oatmeal you can enjoy over the morning paper or a healthy egg wrap you can grab and reheat at the office. Making a few mornings' meals ahead and refrigerating them will help keep you on track during the week.

**8 Don't forget snacks.** Take the time to prepare a few go-to munchies to stash in the fridge or pantry. Cut up long-lasting veggies like carrots, cucumber, and fennel into sticks for noshing or dipping in hummus. Prepare a healthy sweet like our Fruit-and-grain snack bars (page 189) to take on the road. And measure and pack up snacks like nuts, trail mix, or baked chips in small zip-close bags or containers; mark the SmartPoints® value on each to streamline your tracking.

**9 Visit a farmers' market.** Weekends are a good time to combine shopping with getting to know the producers in your area. Local, in-season produce is usually offered no more than a day or two after it's picked, meaning it's likely to stay fresher throughout the week than supermarket produce. It's also a great way to try out new items you might not be familiar with.

**10 Enlist a buddy.** A friend or family member with similar health or cooking goals can be an excellent source of support. Make plans to batch-cook together, or agree to each make double of a different recipe and swap the extras.

## Shopping

Great meals start with great ingredients, so plan to make grocery shopping as enjoyable and stress-free as possible. A few smart strategies will make it easier and keep you on track.

## Before you go

**Get inspired by recipes.** Start by paging through the chapters of this book, visiting WW.com, and thinking about favorite recipes you can adapt for healthy eating. Gather a few options and make them the start of your shopping list.

**Check sales online.** Look through the weekly specials, especially for in-season produce, offered at your favorite stores. You can even sign up for sales alerts to be sent directly to your phone. Plan a few more recipes based on what's economical and seasonal.

**Shop with a buddy.** Go with a friend or family member who shares your health goals or who'd like to split purchases at a wholesale club. Include a quick stop for coffee or a stroll through a park, or plan to cook or prep together afterward.

**Bring your own bags.** Sturdy bags with durable handles will make carrying your groceries more comfortable, may earn you a small discount at stores, and will protect your food on the way home. Take an insulated bag to keep perishables fresher and frozen items ice-cold.

**Commit to your list.** Most grocery stores are designed to get you to buy more food, not less or healthier food. That's why planning is essential. Take a list—even if it's only notes on your phone—to keep yourself on track.

**Don't shop hungry—or thirsty.** You'll make better decisions when you aren't distracted by cravings. Bring in a bottle filled with water or another healthful beverage to sip as you shop.

**Explore local farmers' markets** and specialty stores for great customer service, as well as to get inspired by and connect with your area's local produce and producers.

**For stay-at-home convenience,** you can use online shopping services that deliver groceries right to your door.

## In the aisles

**Start with produce.** You may know the formula that half your plate should be devoted to fruits and vegetables, but have you ever applied that formula to your grocery purchases? If not, start now. Fruits and vegetables should make up about 50% of your cart or basket. And this is one place where veering off your list is encouraged: If you see an intriguing new fruit or an irresistible display of in-season vegetables, help yourself!

**Choose some long-lasting fruits and veggies.** Most produce is best when eaten within a few days of purchase, but not all: Carrots, cabbage, winter squash, onions, potatoes, apples, watermelon, jicama, beets, celery, and radishes, to name a few, can last for weeks when properly stored. Stocking up on these items will give you ingredients to fall back on if you run out of more perishable items.

**Take advantage of bulk bins.** Grains, beans, nuts, dried fruits, and spices are often available in the bulk bin area of supermarkets, and they're generally less expensive than their packaged counterparts. Plus, you'll bag up just what you need, so you won't pay for more than you'll use.

**Stock up on frozen and canned foods.** Picking up frozen veggies, beans, and more ensures you'll always have the makings of a healthy meal. Frozen unsweetened fruits are an affordable luxury when your favorites are out of season, and unseasoned frozen grains can become speedy sides on busy weeknights. Some of the veggies that hold their quality best when frozen include green peas, sweet corn, artichoke hearts, kale, and pureed butternut squash.

**Don't forget beverages.** Sparkling and infused waters, herbal teas, or even special coffee beans can add variety to your day. Having some of these on hand is a great weight-loss strategy: A 0 SmartPoints drink can often take the place of a snack when you feel you need a little something.

## Back home again

**Prep for healthy snacking.** Put healthy nibbles out where you can see them: A bowl of fruit on the counter and cut-up vegetables in clear plastic containers at eye level in the fridge are smart options. If you bought nuts or dried fruit, transfer them to single-serving bags and label them with their SmartPoints values for foolproof tracking and portion control.

**Keep the momentum going!** Seek out more healthy recipes to try and start planning your next trip. Your cooking and weight-loss successes will make each excursion more rewarding than the last.

# Must-have grocery staples

Having a well-stocked pantry, refrigerator, and freezer is beyond helpful for weight loss, so commit to filling them with the kinds of healthful foods you and your family want. To get started, take an inventory of what you already have on hand. Chances are you have many of the delicious, versatile ingredients used in the tips and recipes throughout this book. Read through our suggestions below and see what makes sense for your individual WW plan and your lifestyle. As you expand your pantry, shopping will take less time each week.

## Stock the pantry

- Pantry items last a long time, so if your budget and storage space allow, create a stash of items like canned beans, broths, tomato products, light coconut milk, tuna, salmon, and anchovies; dried pasta and noodles; rice and other grains; jarred olives, capers, and roasted red peppers; and oils and vinegars.

- Go-to basics like breadcrumbs, flours, baking powder, sugar, hot sauce, and dried herbs and spices are essential. If you love Asian-inspired foods, keep a supply of soy sauce, hoisin sauce, chili-garlic sauce or gochujang, curry paste, and sesame oil.

- Pantry produce basics are the workhorses of the kitchen, so always have a few onions, potatoes, sweet potatoes, shallots, and a head of garlic on hand. Storing them in a basket in a cool cupboard will help them stay fresh for weeks.

- Convenience foods make cooking healthy meals a possibility when you feel you have no time. As well as the usual canned tomatoes, canned beans, and broths mentioned above, short-cut ingredients such as marinara sauce, bottled salsas, pre-baked pizza crusts, and quick-cooking rice and other grains are must-haves for quick meals.

- Nuts are great flavor, texture, and nutrient enhancers. Just a sprinkling can take a dish to the next level, so stock a few favorites: Almonds, walnuts, pecans, hazelnuts, pine nuts, or peanuts are all versatile and often interchangeable. Seeds like chia, pepitas, sesame, and ground flax are also terrific, particularly in breakfast dishes. Buy nuts and seeds in small quantities. If storing them for longer than a few weeks, pop them in the freezer. And keep portions small: All nuts and seeds are high in SmartPoints®.

## Stock the fridge

- Always keep on hand basics like low-fat milk, yogurt, and cheese; eggs; ketchup and mustard; reduced-fat mayonnaise; and butter.

- Weeknight meals call for quick-cooking vegetables. Buy a few of these each week for recipes and side dishes: asparagus, baby carrots, bell peppers, broccoli, Brussels sprouts, cauliflower, green beans, kale, snow peas, spinach, yellow squash, and zucchini. For easy cooking and serving suggestions, see "Make the most of vegetables," page xxx.

- Keep a selection of fresh fruits to incorporate into salads and main dishes, and for snacks throughout the day. Apples, pears, kiwis, and citrus are all long-keeping, delicious for snacking, and versatile for cooking.

- Fresh herbs add bright fragrance and flavor and a hit of color that's not matched by their dried counterparts. Try to keep parsley on hand and one or two other favorite herbs. If you can, grow your own: An outdoor herb garden takes up only a small space, or you can grow herbs indoors in pots near a sunny window.

- Don't forget refrigerated convenience foods, such as prepared pesto, salsa, shredded cheese, fresh pasta, pre-washed salad greens, coleslaw mix, prepped butternut squash, and pre-cooked lentils and beets.

## Stock the freezer

- Keeping a stash of healthy frozen foods means fewer trips to the supermarket, and if you buy when foods are on sale or when you visit a wholesale club, you'll save money. Meats, poultry, and seafood spoil quickly in the refrigerator, so buy a couple of items fresh for early in the week, then rely on foods from the freezer for later in the week.

- Chicken breasts and thighs, turkey cutlets, steaks, pork chops, fish fillets, shrimp, and fruits and veggies are essential staples for your freezer.

Mushroom-barley soup with red miso, page 45

# Packing for meals on the go

Out for the day or the evening? Eating at school or the office or having a family meal at a park or event is often healthier and more enjoyable when you don't have to rely on restaurants or fast food. It can save you a bundle, and tracking can be simpler and more accurate. Here are tried-and-true strategies to put into your daily and weekly routine.

**Start with a plan** Set aside time once a week or so to map out a strategy for the DIY meals you and your family prefer. Research what produce is in season, cull some recipes you'd like to try, and poll other members of your household about what healthy meals they like. Once you've got your ideas together, make a shopping list.

**Make the most of leftovers** When you cook, think about doubling your recipe and refrigerating or freezing extras to enjoy later. Dividing the food into individual portions and clearly labeling them with the dish's name and the SmartPoints value before freezing is the best approach.

**Get the right gear** A paper bag, a simple lunch box, or a repurposed take-out container... These items are all you really need when you want to pack up a meal, but it's both fun and practical to give yourself a few more options. Check out the collection of WW essentials, such as the Make It and Take It Kit, on our Amazon store or WW.com/shop.

## Packed lunch 101

How to get that delicious lunch (or dinner) from here to there in mouthwatering shape? We share our pro tips.

### Salads

- A salad loves to travel in a roomy container, one that won't mash individual ingredients and that's big enough to actually seal and shake the whole thing when you're ready to dress and eat.
- Pack dressing on the side to help keep everything fresh and crisp. A twist-top dressing container makes a safe, leak-proof seal; consider saving and repurposing a small glass jar (a spice jar or baby-food jar is ideal).
- Got room at your desk to store a few extras? Stock a mini pantry with salt, pepper, soy sauce, and maybe your favorite hot sauce to perk up your packed lunches.
- Think about using washable and reusable utensils instead of disposable plastic whenever you can.

### Soups & stews

- Choose a thermos to keep soups or stews hot for several hours. A wide-mouth thermos is ideal; you can eat right out of it instead of having to transfer your food to another container. Make sure your food is piping hot when you pack it.
- If a microwave is available, a microwave-safe container like a heavy glass bowl with a leak-proof lid is good to carry your meal to work. Keep it well chilled until you're ready to reheat it. Remove the lid, cover lightly with a damp paper towel, and reheat thoroughly.
- Extras like bread, crackers, croutons, or tortilla chips like to ride separately so they stay crisp.
- Delicate toppings like herbs can be wrapped in a paper towel to stay moist.
- Pack a reusable soup spoon when you can so you won't have to resort to a disposable one.

# About our recipes

While losing weight isn't only about what you eat, WW realizes the critical role it plays in your success and overall good health. That's why our philosophy is to offer great-tasting, easy recipes that are nutritious as well as delicious. Our recipes are designed to encourage a healthier pattern of eating with lots of ZeroPoint™ foods and lower SmartPoints® value ingredients to make the most of your Budget. If you have special dietary needs, consult with your healthcare professional, then adapt our recipes for your needs.

## Get started, keep going, and enjoy delicious food

At WW, we believe that eating well makes life better, no matter where you are in your weight-loss journey. Unlike other weight-loss programs, which focus solely on calories, the SmartPoints system guides you toward a healthier pattern of eating. But this isn't a diet—all food is "in." Eating well should be fun and energizing, so that healthier choices become second nature. For maximum satisfaction, keep in mind:

- On the *myWW*™ program, there's room for all foods (ones that are ZeroPoint and ones that have SmartPoints)—variety is key to a healthy and livable eating style.
- SmartPoints values are given for each recipe. The SmartPoints value for each ingredient is assigned based on the number of calories and the amount of saturated fat, sugar, and protein in each ingredient. The SmartPoints values for each ingredient are then added together and divided by the number of servings, and the result is rounded.
- Recipes include approximate nutritional information: They are analyzed for Calories (Cal), Total Fat, Saturated Fat (Sat Fat), Sodium (Sod), Total Carbohydrates (Total Carb), Sugar, Dietary Fiber (Fib), and Protein (Prot). These values come from the WW database, which is maintained by registered dietitians.
- Recipe introductory headnote suggestions and tips have a SmartPoints value of 0 unless otherwise stated.
- For more information about the WW program, please visit WW.com/us/m/cms/plan-basics.

## Calculations not what you expected?

SmartPoints values for the recipes in this book are calculated without taking the ZeroPoint foods into account—fruits, most vegetables, and some lean proteins that are part of the program. However, the nutritional information does include the nutrient content of these ingredients. This means you may notice discrepancies with the SmartPoints value you calculate using the nutrition information provided for the recipe versus the SmartPoints value listed for the recipe. That's because the SmartPoints values for the recipes that contain ZeroPoint ingredients have been adjusted to reflect those ingredients, while the nutrition information provided includes the nutrition for all of the ingredients. For tracking purposes, use the SmartPoints value listed for the recipe. When fruits and veggies are liquefied or pureed (as in a smoothie), they are no longer ZeroPoint foods; that's because they don't fill you up as much. So recipes for things you drink or sip may have higher SmartPoints values.

Alcohol is included in our SmartPoints calculations. Because nutrition information for alcohol is generally not included on nutrition labels, it's not an option you can include when using the handheld or online SmartPoints calculator or the WW app. We include alcohol information that we get from our database, so you may see discrepancies between SmartPoints you see in our recipes and values you get using the calculator. The SmartPoints listed for our recipes are the most accurate.

### Look for these icons throughout the book to choose the recipes that best fit your needs.

**Vegetarian:** Recipes that contain no animal-flesh foods or products made from animal flesh, though they may contain eggs and dairy products.

**Vegan:** Recipes that contain no animal-flesh foods, eggs, dairy products, or honey.

**Gluten-free:** Recipes that contain no wheat, barley, or rye, or any products made from these ingredients. (Always check the label on ingredients that are inherently gluten-free—such as broth and spices—but could contain gluten depending on the manufacturer.)

**Dairy-free:** Recipes that contain no milk from any animal and no products made from animal milk.

**Nut-free:** Recipes that contain no tree nuts or peanuts.

*Note: Recipes conform to the icon designations, but tip and serving suggestions may not.*

**Fruit-and-nut granola,**
**page 14**

# Get the gear for healthy cooking

The first step to creating great meals? Equip your kitchen with the tools that streamline everyday cooking. You may already have many of these go-to items; a few of the appliances we recommend (like an Instant Pot® and countertop air fryer) are nice to have, but definitely not essential. Aside from the basics, here are some tools worth investing in for easier, healthier cooking.

**Blender or food processor**
Each purées nicely, so strictly speaking you don't need both—if space is tight, choose the one you'll use more often. A blender works best with liquids (think smoothies or soups), while a processor excels at chopping, mincing, and slicing.

**Citrus juicer**
Fresh lemon or lime juice adds zing to countless dishes.

**Countertop air fryer**
Fantastic for crisping everything from onion rings to breaded cutlets, with minimal (or no) added fat.

**Dutch oven**
For making vegetable or bean-filled soups, stews, and braises.

**Grill pan**
A stovetop grill pan requires little added fat and allows any excess to drain away.

### Instant Pot

There's a reason it's the of-the-moment kitchen gadget. This electric pressure cooker also works as a rice cooker and slow cooker, and even makes yogurt. We love using it to shave off time for dried beans and grains.

### Knives

You need three: a chef's knife for chopping, a paring knife for precise jobs, and a long serrated knife for bread and delicate items like tomatoes.

### Knife sharpener

You can use an old-fashioned sharpening stone or try a manual or electric sharpener—whatever fits your style and budget. A rod-shaped "steel" is great for honing your knife blade between sharpenings.

### Microplane

This small rasp-like grater is ideal for zesting citrus and mincing fresh ginger or garlic cloves.

### Muffin tin

Not just for muffins! The individual compartments offer built-in portion control for individual-size casseroles and meatloaves too. Mini-muffin tins make perfectly portioned two-bite treats.

### Parchment paper

It's heat-safe and treated so it's nonstick and water-resistant. Use it instead of greasing baking sheets.

### Slow cooker

The classic "just push start" appliance for simmering and braising while you're out.

### Steamer basket

Used in the Instant Pot or in a saucepan on the stove, it lets you cook vegetables, fish, and more without added fat.

### Wooden spoons

The most versatile: Perfect for stirring in a nonstick pan without scratching it, plus much, much more.

# Season strategically

Keeping your pantry stocked with spices, herbs, and other seasonings means that even a humble chicken breast can taste different every night of the week. Many countries' staple seasonings overlap, but each region has its own way of combining and layering flavors. The following profiles (all 0 SmartPoints®) can help you stock the basics for your favorite go-to cuisines.

**Caribbean**
- allspice
- bay leaves
- cayenne
- cinnamon
- cloves
- ginger
- hot pepper sauce
- lime juice
- nutmeg
- Scotch bonnet peppers
- thyme, fresh or dried
- turmeric

**China**
- chili-garlic sauce
- ginger
- rice vinegar
- soy sauce
- star anise
- Szechuan peppercorns

**France**
- bay leaves
- Dijon mustard
- herbes de Provence
- rosemary
- sage
- shallots
- tarragon
- thyme

**Greece**
- bay leaves
- cinnamon
- dill
- lemon juice and zest
- mint
- oregano

**India**
- cardamom
- cilantro
- coriander
- cumin
- curry powder
- garam masala
- ginger
- turmeric

**Italy**
- basil
- capers
- oregano
- red pepper flakes
- red wine vinegar
- rosemary
- sage
- thyme

**Japan**
- ginger
- miso paste
- rice vinegar
- soy sauce
- wasabi paste

**Korea**
- fish sauce
- ginger
- gochujang chile paste
- soy sauce

**Mexico**
- ancho chile powder
- chili powder
- chipotles en adobo
- cilantro
- coriander
- cumin
- fresh chiles
- lime juice
- oregano

**Middle East**
- Aleppo pepper
- cloves
- coriander
- cumin
- mint
- nutmeg
- paprika
- parsley
- preserved lemons
- sumac

**Morocco**
- allspice
- cayenne
- cinnamon
- coriander
- cumin
- ginger
- harissa
- preserved lemons
- ras el hanout

**Spain**
- oregano
- paprika (smoked, sweet, and hot)
- saffron
- sherry vinegar

**Thailand**
- basil
- cilantro
- fish sauce
- fresh chiles
- lemongrass
- lime
- mint
- shallots
- soy sauce

# Shortcuts to flavor

Each of these global blends will season 4 to 6 skinless boneless chicken breasts or fish fillets. Sprinkle on, then use immediately or refrigerate up to 1 hour before grilling, baking, or sautéing.

**Greek**

2 tsp dried oregano + 1 tsp lemon zest + 1 tsp dried dill + ½ tsp garlic powder + ½ tsp salt + ¼ tsp black pepper

**Middle Eastern**

2 tsp cumin + 1 tsp black pepper + 1 tsp coriander + 1 tsp paprika + ½ tsp salt + ¼ tsp ground cardamom + ⅛ tsp ground cloves + ⅛ tsp ground nutmeg

**Mexican**

2 tsp chili powder + 2 tsp cumin + 1 tsp dried oregano + 1 tsp ancho chile powder + 1 tsp garlic powder + ½ tsp salt

**Italian**

1 tsp dried oregano + 1 tsp dried basil + 1 tsp dried thyme + 1 tsp garlic powder + ½ tsp salt + ½ tsp dried rosemary, crushed + ¼ tsp black pepper + ⅛ tsp red pepper flakes

**Thai marinade**

¼ cup fish sauce + 3 Tbsp reduced-sodium soy sauce + 2 garlic cloves + 1 stalk lemongrass (white part only) + 8–10 cilantro stems; combine all in a food processor

# 8 must-have recipes

We gathered our favorite foundational recipes that are easy, versatile, and delicious. Homemade staples like dressings and sauces, beans and grains, and broths can make everyday meals more interesting—and more healthful. If you spend the effort putting together a terrific salad, why open a bottle of store-bought dressing when you can whisk up your own in minutes? And why overpay for bottled tomato sauce (often hiding added sugar) and canned beans when your own versions taste better and stay at the ready in the fridge or freezer? Having these items on hand will give your meals a running start and encourage you to improvise!

## Italian vinaigrette

This vinaigrette is perfect drizzled over steamed green beans or asparagus, or used as a dressing for almost any green salad, bean salad, or whole-grain salad. Getting ready to grill? Make the vinaigrette your go-to marinade.

**Prep 5 min  Cook 0 min  Serves 8**

2 2 2

- **¼ cup minced shallots (about 2 shallots)**
- **¼ cup red wine vinegar**
- **¼ cup vegetable broth or water**
- **3 tablespoons extra-virgin olive oil**
- **1 teaspoon dried Italian seasoning blend**
- **½ teaspoon sugar**
- **½ teaspoon salt**
- **¼ teaspoon black pepper**

Combine all ingredients in small jar with tight-fitting lid. Seal jar and shake until mixed well. Can be refrigerated up to 4 days. Shake well before using.

Per serving (1½ tablespoons): 52 Cal, 5 g Total Fat, 0 g Sat Fat, 164 mg Sod, 1 g Total Carb, 1 g Sugar, 0 g Fib, 0 g Prot.

## Ranch dip

Who doesn't love a good ranch dip? Ours is thick and creamy—just like the original—but low in SmartPoints®. Serve it as a salad dressing, as a dip, or as a sauce for grilled everything.

**Prep 20 min  Cook 0 min  Serves 6**

- **½ cup low-fat buttermilk**
- **6 tablespoons light mayonnaise**
- **1 garlic clove, minced**
- **3 tablespoons chopped fresh chives**
- **2 tablespoons chopped fresh flat-leaf parsley**
- **½ teaspoon cider vinegar**
- **¼ teaspoon salt**
- **⅛ teaspoon black pepper**

Whisk together all ingredients in small bowl. Cover and refrigerate about 10 minutes to allow flavors to blend. Can be stored in covered jar up to 1 week. Shake before using. (Makes generous ¾ cup)

Per serving (2 tablespoons): 46 Cal, 4 g Total Fat, 10 g Sat Fat, 252 mg Sod, 3 g Total Carb, 2 g Sugar, 0 g Fib, 1 g Prot.

## Classic Italian tomato sauce

Our sauce uses cans of whole peeled tomatoes (look for San Marzano for fantastic flavor) along with onion and garlic. It's excellent over any pasta shape for a quick weeknight supper and amazing spooned onto grilled eggplant topped with grated Parmesan or your favorite meatballs.

**Prep 10 min  Cook 30 min  Serves 12**

- **1 tablespoon olive oil**
- **2 medium onions, chopped**
- **4 garlic cloves, minced**
- **2 (28-ounce) cans whole peeled tomatoes, drained and broken up**
- **¼ cup tomato paste**
- **1 teaspoon salt**
- **½ teaspoon black pepper**

1 Heat oil in Dutch oven over medium heat. Add onions and cook, stirring frequently, until softened, about 5 minutes. Add garlic and cook, stirring constantly, until fragrant, about 30 seconds.

2 Add all remaining ingredients to Dutch oven and bring to boil. Reduce heat and simmer, partially covered, until flavors are blended and sauce is slightly thickened, about 25 minutes.

Per serving (½ cup): 46 Cal, 1 g Total Fat, 0 g Sat Fat, 385 mg Sod, 8 g Total Carb, 5 g Sugar, 20 g Fib, 2 g Prot.

## Lemony tahini sauce

Tahini is a classic in falafel sandwiches and other Middle Eastern dishes, but this rich, tangy sauce can do so much more: Turn to it as a dressing for salad or grain bowls, drizzle it over grilled meats or vegetables, or use it to sauce roasted or pan-seared chicken breasts.

**Prep 5 min  Cook 0 min  Serves 8**

- **6 tablespoons tahini**
- **6 tablespoons lemon juice**
- **¼ cup warm vegetable broth**
- **2 small garlic cloves, minced**
- **¾ teaspoon ground cumin**
- **½ teaspoon salt**
- **Pinch cayenne**

Whisk together all ingredients until

Italian vinaigrette

Classic Italian tomato sauce, page xxiv

Lemony tahini sauce, page xxiv

Perfect rice

Beans from scratch

smooth. Whisk in water or more broth a teaspoon at a time if mixture is too thick to pour easily. Will keep refrigerated up to 4 days.

Per serving (2 tablespoons): 79 Cal, 6 g Total Fat, 1 g Sat Fat, 167 mg Sod, 3 g Total Carb, 0 g Sugar, 1 g Fib, 2 g Prot.

## Perfect rice

Making perfectly fluffy white—or brown—rice is easier than you think. And you don't need a rice cooker... just your favorite saucepan. Cooked rice isn't just good as a side; you can add it to soups, stews, or braises or use it as a base for a quick fried rice dish. You can also whip up a hearty rice salad by stirring in parsley, halved cherry tomatoes, and cooked shrimp or diced chicken or turkey breast.

**Prep 15 min  Cook 18–30 min**
**Serves 6 (white rice) or 5 (brown rice)**

### White rice

3 3 3

**2 cups water**
**¼ teaspoon salt, or to taste**
**1 cup long-grain white rice**

### Brown rice

4 4 0

**10 cups water**
**1 teaspoon salt, or to taste**
**1 cup long-grain brown rice**

**To make white rice,** bring water and salt to boil in small saucepan. Add rice and stir to separate grains. Reduce heat and simmer, covered, 18 minutes. Remove saucepan from heat and let stand, covered, 5–10 minutes or until ready to serve. Fluff with fork just before serving. (Makes 3 cups)

**To make brown rice,** bring water and salt to boil in large saucepan. Add rice and stir to separate grains. Reduce heat and simmer, uncovered, 30 minutes. Drain rice in sieve and quickly return to pot with water clinging to rice. Cover and let stand at least 10 minutes or up to 30 minutes. Fluff with fork just before serving. (Makes 2½ cups)

Per serving (½ cup white rice): 113 Cal, 0 g Total Fat, 0 g Sat Fat, 98 mg Sod, 25 g Total Carb, 0 g Sugar, 1 g Fib, 2 g Prot.

Per serving (½ cup brown rice): 136 Cal, 1 g Total Fat, 0 g Sat Fat, 118 mg Sod, 28 g Total Carb, 0 g Sugar, 1 g Fib, 3 g Prot.

## Beans from scratch

This is the easiest way to prepare dried beans. They're worth the effort because they have better flavor and texture than canned, and they're much easier on your wallet, so give them a try if you're not already a convert. Cooking up a 1-pound batch means you have enough to add to soups, stews, rice dishes, or grain bowls for a quick protein boost.

**Prep 5 min  Cook 45 min–2 hrs**
**Serves 12**

3 0 0 

**1 (1-pound) bag dried beans, such as red kidney, small white, chickpeas, cannellini, pinto, or black**
**2–3 garlic cloves, peeled**
**2 bay leaves**
**1 teaspoon salt**

**1** Place beans in a sieve and rinse under cool running water; drain.

**2** Transfer beans to a large pot; add enough water to cover by 4 inches. Add garlic, bay leaves, and salt and bring to boil over high heat. Reduce heat and cook, partially covered, at gentle simmer, until beans are just tender, 45 minutes–2 hours, depending on variety of beans. Remove from heat and let cool to room temperature. Transfer beans with their liquid to airtight containers. Refrigerate up to 4 days or freeze up to 3 months.

Per serving (½ cup): 130 Cal, 1 g Total Fat, 0 g Sat Fat, 196 mg Sod, 24 g Total Carb, 1 g Sugar, 6 g Fib, 8 g Prot.

## Slow cooker vegetable broth

**Prep 12 min  Cook 4–10 hrs  Serves 6**

0 0 0 

This easy-to-prepare broth has a rich, slightly sweet flavor from carrots and onions and subtle earthiness from mushrooms. Use it in any recipe that calls for vegetable broth or as a substitute for chicken broth. It's excellent for soups and stews—or turn to it instead of water when you cook rice or other grains. Don't have a slow cooker? Place all the ingredients in a large pot and bring to a boil. Reduce the heat, cover, and simmer, about 1 hour.

**3 large carrots, scrubbed and cut into 2-inch lengths**
**3 large celery stalks with leaves, cut into 2-inch lengths**
**2 large onions, unpeeled and quartered**
**2 cups sliced mushrooms**
**4 large garlic cloves, unpeeled and lightly crushed with side of knife**
**8 whole black peppercorns**
**1 teaspoon kosher salt, or to taste**
**8 cups water**
**¼ teaspoon black pepper, or to taste**

**1** Combine carrots, celery, onions, mushrooms, garlic, peppercorns, and salt in 5- or 6-quart slow cooker. Add water. Cover and cook 4–5 hours on High or 8–10 hours on Low.

**2** Ladle vegetables and broth through large sieve set over large bowl. Discard vegetables and peppercorns. Add black pepper to broth. Let broth cool to room temperature, then pour into airtight containers or 1-quart mason jars. Cover and refrigerate up to several days or freeze up to 3 months.

**Slow cooker vegetable broth,** **page xxvii**

**Slow cooker chicken broth**

Per serving (1 cup): 49 Cal, 0 g Total Fat, 0 g Sat Fat, 385 mg Sod, 11 g Total Carb, 5 g Sugar, 3 g Fib, 2 g Prot.

## Slow cooker chicken broth

**Prep 12 min Cook 4–10 hrs Serves 8**

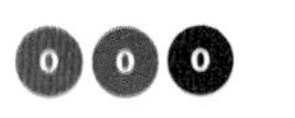

No store-bought broth can compare to the rich flavor, silky texture, and golden color of homemade. Using a slow cooker means there's no checking and no stirring. For easy use, transfer the broth to mason jars and refrigerate up to 1 week or freeze up to 4 months. Use it in any recipe that calls for canned chicken broth, or drink a mug of the warm broth as a nice change from coffee or tea. Don't have a slow cooker? Place all the ingredients in a large pot and bring to a boil. Reduce the heat, cover, and simmer until the chicken and vegetables are tender, about 1 hour.

**4 pounds cut-up, bone-in chicken parts (breasts and legs)**
**2 medium onions, unpeeled and quartered**
**2 large carrots, scrubbed and quartered**
**2 large celery stalks with leaves, quartered**
**3 large garlic cloves, unpeeled and lightly crushed with side of knife**
**12 whole black peppercorns**
**1 teaspoon kosher salt, or to taste**
**8 cups water**

1 Place chicken in 5- or 6-quart slow cooker. Add onions, carrots, celery, garlic, peppercorns, and salt. Pour in water. Cover and cook 4–5 hours on High or 8–10 hours on Low.

2 Using slotted spoon, transfer chicken to large plate or bowl. When cool enough to handle, remove and discard skin and bones. Put chicken meat in airtight container and refrigerate for another use, if you'd like. Ladle vegetables and broth through large sieve set over large bowl. Discard vegetables and peppercorns. Let broth cool to room temperature; cover and refrigerate overnight.

3 The next day, remove and discard solid fat from surface of broth. Transfer broth to airtight containers or 1-quart mason jars. Cover and refrigerate up to several days or freeze up to 3 months.

Per serving (1 cup): 12 Cal, 0 g Total Fat, 0 g Sat Fat, 553 mg Sod, 1 g Total Carb, 1 g Sugar, 0 g Fib, 2 g Prot.

Ranch dip, page xxiv

# Make the most of vegetables

Most fresh veggies are ZeroPoint™ foods, which means you can enjoy these delicious, easy-to-prepare sides as much as you'd like. We show you which method works best for cooking the most common vegetables (some are great several ways) and give four basic, but never boring, recipes to get you started.

## Grilled broccoli

**Prep 10 min Cook 8 min Serves 4**

Preheat grill to medium-high or prepare medium-high fire. Trim **2 pounds broccoli** and cut into 1-inch florets. Lightly spray broccoli with **olive oil nonstick spray;** sprinkle with **½ teaspoon salt.** Place in grill basket or on grill rack and grill, turning occasionally, until crisp-tender, 6–8 minutes. Transfer to large bowl. Add squeeze of **lemon** or **lime juice,** sprinkle of **red pepper flakes,** or dash of **soy sauce,** if desired, and toss to coat. Per serving: about 1¼ cups

**Veggies that are great to grill**

Cut any of the following vegetables into long slices or rounds (eggplant, summer squash, tomatoes), or large pieces (bell peppers, onions) or bite-size pieces (broccoli, fennel). Keep the following whole: asparagus, corn on the cob, snow peas, sugar snap peas, scallions, and cherry tomatoes. If you prefer, use a grill basket for any of these except the whole corn on the cob and especially for smaller pieces of veggies. Season and grill as in Grilled broccoli. Cook times may vary; depending on the vegetable and your taste, you can cook until softened, crisp-tender, or lightly charred.

**Asparagus, Bell peppers, Broccoli, Corn (on cob), Eggplant, Fennel, Mushrooms, Onions, Peas (snow peas, sugar snap peas), Scallions, Summer squash (yellow squash, zucchini), Tomatoes (regular, plum, cherry, grape, campari)**

## Sautéed green beans

**Prep 10 min Cook 10 min Serves 4**

Heat **2 teaspoons olive oil** in large skillet over medium-high heat. Add half of **1 pound green beans, trimmed,** and cook, stirring frequently, until tender, 3–5 minutes (add a few tablespoons of water, if needed). Transfer beans to large bowl. Repeat with remaining green beans. Add **½ teaspoon salt** and **¼ teaspoon black pepper** to beans and toss to coat. Add squeeze of **lemon juice** and/or sprinkle of **fresh chopped basil, chives, oregano, parsley, tarragon,** or **thyme,** if desired, and toss to coat. Per serving: generous ¾ cup

**Veggies that are great to sauté**

Cut any of the following vegetables into bite-size pieces and sauté and season as in Sautéed green beans. Try adding chopped onion and/or garlic and mixing a couple of different veggies together. Cook times may vary; depending on the vegetable and your taste, you can cook until soft, crisp-tender, golden, or crunchy.

**Asparagus, Bell peppers, Cabbage (green, red, savoy), Corn (kernels), Delicate greens (spinach, watercress), Eggplant, Fennel, Green beans, Leeks, Mushrooms Onions, Peas (snow peas, sugar snap peas), Radishes Scallions, Sturdy greens (collards, kale, mustard greens, radicchio, Swiss chard), Summer squash (yellow squash, zucchini), Tomatoes (regular, plum, cherry, grape, campari)**

## Steamed carrots

**Prep 5 min Cook 10 min Serves 4**

Peel and trim **1 bunch (about 6) carrots.** Halve the carrots lengthwise and place in a steamer basket. Set basket in saucepan over 1 inch of **boiling water.** Cover pan and steam until just tender when poked with the tip of a knife, 8–10 minutes. Transfer to plate; top with **2 teaspoons unsalted butter** and toss until melted. Sprinkle with **1 tablespoon chopped fresh parsley or carrot tops, ½ teaspoon coarse sea salt,** and **¼ teaspoon black pepper.** Per serving: about 3 halves

### Veggies that are great to steam

Cut any of the following vegetables into bite-size pieces or lengths that will fit into the steamer basket. Steam and season as in Steamed carrots. Try mixing two or three different veggies together. Cook times may vary; depending on the vegetable and your taste, you can cook until softened, tender, or just wilted for the delicate greens.

**Artichokes, Asparagus, Beets, Broccoli, Cabbage (green, red, savoy), Carrots, Cauliflower, Delicate greens (spinach, watercress), Green beans, Leeks, Peas (snow peas, sugar snap peas), Potatoes, Sturdy greens (collards, kale, mustard greens, radicchio, Swiss chard), Summer squash (yellow squash, zucchini), Winter squash (acorn, butternut, Hubbard, kabocha, spaghetti)**

## Roasted Brussels sprouts

**Prep 10 min Cook 30 min Serves 4**

Preheat oven to 375°F. Spray large rimmed baking sheet with **nonstick spray.** Combine **1 pound trimmed halved Brussels sprouts, 1 tablespoon olive oil, 1/2 teaspoon salt,** and **1/2 teaspoon black pepper** on prepared pan and toss. Spread to form even layer; roast until tender, stirring occasionally, about 30 minutes. Transfer to large bowl. Add **lemon juice,** if desired, and toss to coat. Per serving: about ¾ cup

### Veggies that are great to roast

Cut any of the following vegetables into bite-size pieces or 2-inch lengths or chunks. Season and roast as in Roasted Brussels sprouts. If you mix different veggies together, make sure they will all take about the same time to cook. Cook times may vary; depending on the vegetable and your taste, you can cook until softened, lightly browned, or golden brown. Note: Beets can bleed color, so keep them to one side of the pan if you're roasting them with another vegetable.

**Artichokes, Asparagus, Beets, Bell peppers, Broccoli, Brussels sprouts, Carrots, Cauliflower, Celery root, Corn (on cob or kernels), Eggplant, Fennel, Green beans, Leeks, Mushrooms, Onions, Parsnips, Potatoes, Radishes, Rutabaga, Scallions, Sturdy greens (collards, kale, mustard, radicchio, Swiss chard), Summer squash (yellow squash, zucchini), Tomatoes (cherry, grape, plum, campari), Turnips, Winter squash (acorn, butternut, Hubbard, kabocha, spaghetti)**

Chapter 1

# Breakfast

# Oatmeal made easy | Recipe builder

START WITH THE BASE

## Old-fashioned oatmeal 2 ways

**Prep 3 min  Cook 3–7 min  Serves 1**

**Stovetop method:** Bring **1 cup water** and **pinch of salt** to boil in small saucepan set over medium heat. Stir in **½ cup old-fashioned (rolled) oats.** Cook, stirring occasionally, until water is absorbed and oats are tender, about 5 minutes. Makes ¾ cup.

**Microwave method:** Combine **1 cup water, pinch of salt,** and **½ cup old-fashioned (rolled) oats** in 2-cup microwavable bowl. Microwave on High until water is absorbed and oats are tender, 2½–3 minutes. Stir and let stand 1 minute. Makes ¾ cup.

BUILD YOUR BOWL

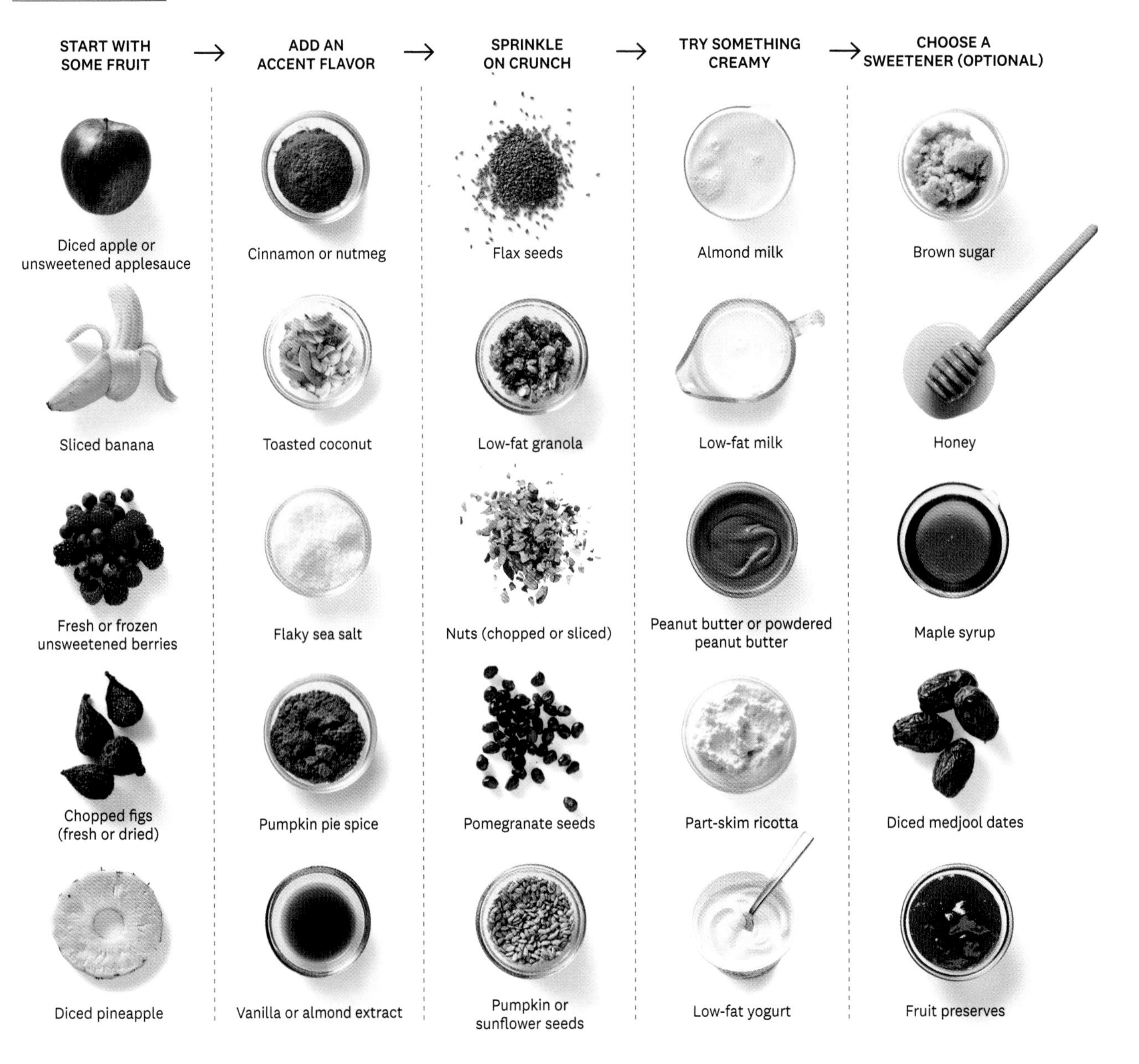

# Some toppings we love

### Apple, pecan, and cinnamon

3 3 3

1 diced apple + ⅛ teaspoon cinnamon + 1 tablespoon chopped pecans + 2 tablespoons fat-free vanilla Greek yogurt

### Fig, honey, and almond

3 3 3

2 quartered fresh figs + large pinch nutmeg + 1 tablespoon sliced almonds + 2 tablespoons part-skim ricotta + 1 teaspoon honey

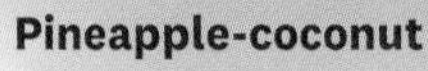

### Pineapple-coconut

¼ cup diced pineapple + large pinch flaky sea salt + 1 tablespoon toasted coconut + ¼ cup plain low-fat Greek yogurt

START WITH THE BASE

## Basic omelette

**Prep 5 min  Cook 3 min  Serves 1**

1 Whisk **2 large eggs, ¼ teaspoon salt, ⅛ teaspoon black pepper,** and **1–2 tablespoons chopped herbs** in bowl.

2 Spray 8-inch nonstick skillet with **nonstick spray;** add **½ teaspoon butter** and set over medium heat; swirl pan. When butter stops foaming, pour eggs into skillet, tilting pan to distribute. Cook, lifting eggs, so uncooked portion can run underneath, about 1 minute. Reduce heat to medium-low and cook until eggs are almost set, 30–60 seconds.

3 Spoon omelette filling (see below for ideas) over half of omelette. Fold unfilled half of egg over filling. Reduce heat to low and cook 1 minute. Run spatula around edge of omelette to release. Gently shake pan to shimmy omelette toward rim; slide omelette onto plate.

FILL YOUR OMELETTE

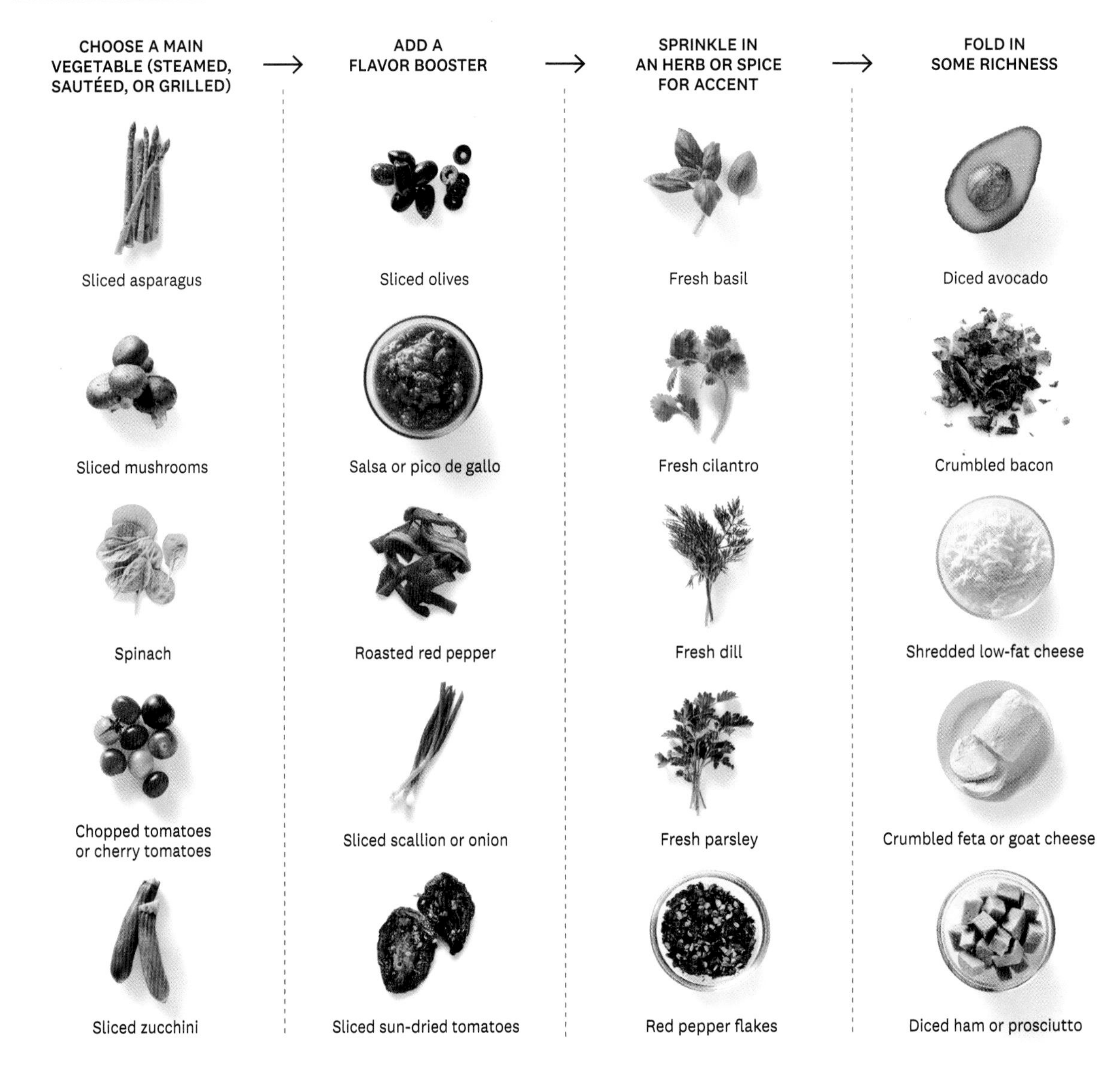

# Some fillings we love

### Spinach, sun-dried tomato, and feta

Mix together ¼ cup steamed spinach + 1 sliced sun-dried tomato (not oil-packed) + pinch red pepper flakes + 2 tablespoons crumbled feta

### Tomato, roasted red pepper, and basil

Mix together 6 halved yellow cherry tomatoes + ¼ cup thinly sliced drained roasted red pepper (not oil-packed) + thinly sliced large basil leaves + ⅓ cup shredded part-skim mozzarella

### Zucchini, goat cheese, and ham

Mix together 1 sliced small zucchini sautéed in 1 teaspoon oil + 1 tablespoon chopped fresh parsley + 2 tablespoons crumbled soft goat cheese + 1 tablespoon diced ham

# Poached eggs with hollandaise and bacon

**Prep 12 min  Cook 14 min  Serves 4**

7 5 5

Our slimmed-down hollandaise makes it easy to enjoy a luxurious, SmartPoints®-friendly version of eggs Benedict. The sauce is also excellent over steamed asparagus or grilled salmon fillets.

- **¼ cup reduced-fat mayonnaise**
- **¼ cup plain fat-free yogurt**
- **1 teaspoon Dijon mustard**
- **½ teaspoon grated lemon zest**
- **1 teaspoon lemon juice**
- **2 teaspoons unsalted butter, softened**
- **1 tablespoon white-wine vinegar**
- **4 large eggs**
- **4 slices Canadian bacon**
- **2 multigrain or whole-wheat English muffins, split and toasted**
- **4 thick slices tomato**
- **2 tablespoons chopped fresh chives (optional)**

**1** To make sauce, whisk together mayonnaise, yogurt, mustard, and lemon zest and juice in small microwavable bowl. Microwave on High until hot, about 30 seconds. Stir in butter until melted. Cover to keep warm.

**2** To poach eggs, fill large deep skillet or sauté pan with water and bring to boil; add vinegar. Reduce heat to bare simmer. Carefully crack eggs, one at a time, into custard cup and slip into water. Cook until whites are firm but yolks are still soft, about 5 minutes. With slotted spoon, transfer eggs, one at a time, to paper towel–lined plate to drain. Cover to keep warm.

**3** Wipe skillet dry with paper towel. Add Canadian bacon and cook over medium-high heat until heated through and browned in spots, about 1 minute per side.

**4** Place English muffin half on each of 4 plates. Top with 1 slice tomato, 1 slice bacon, 1 egg, and about 2 tablespoons sauce. Sprinkle with chives, if using.

**Per serving** (1 eggs Benedict): 248 Cal, 13 g Total Fat, 4 g Sat Fat, 554 mg Sod, 16 g Total Carb, 4 g Sugar, 1 g Fib, 15 g Prot.

## Prep ahead

The hollandaise sauce can be prepared and kept warm for up to 40 minutes before serving.

# Smashed avocado and egg toast

**Prep 5 min  Cook 2 min  Serves 1**

No wonder avocado toast is everywhere: It's a great source of fiber and contains a host of good-for-you vitamins, and the crisp/creamy texture satisfies every time.

**¼ ripe Hass avocado, sliced**
**1 slice whole-grain or whole-wheat bread, toasted**
**1 hard-cooked or soft-cooked large egg, sliced**
**Pinch salt**
**Pinch black pepper**
**Pinch red pepper flakes**

Put avocado slices on toast and gently mash with fork. Arrange sliced egg on top and sprinkle with salt, black pepper, and pepper flakes.

**Per serving** (1 avocado toast): 242 Cal, 14 g Total Fat, 3 g Sat Fat, 503 mg Sod, 19 g Total Carb, 2 g Sugar, 5 g Fib, 11 g Prot.

## Smart pointers

Want a piled-high sandwich? Top the avocado with ultra-thin slices of red onion, tomato, and/or English (seedless) cucumber for no additional SmartPoints®.

# Steel-cut oats with maple labneh

**Prep 8 min  Cook 3 min  Serves 6**

7 7 5

Put your Instant Pot® to work by preparing a batch of our steel-cut oats, even on busy mornings—it cooks in only 3 minutes. We pair it with rich, creamy labneh, a strained yogurt cheese (sometimes called kefir cheese) that's rich in probiotics. Leftover oats can be refrigerated for 3 or 4 days.

**1 cup steel-cut oats**
**2¾ cups water**
**2 (3-inch) cinnamon sticks**
**½ teaspoon vanilla extract**
**½ teaspoon salt**
**¼ teaspoon ground ginger**
**4 Gala or other sweet-crisp apples, cored**
**⅔ cup labneh**
**2½ tablespoons pure maple syrup**
**3 tablespoons chopped walnuts**
**Nutmeg, preferably freshly ground, for sprinkling**

**1** Combine oats, water, cinnamon sticks, vanilla, salt, and ginger in 6-quart Instant Pot. Dice 3 apples and add to pot. Lock lid, making sure vent is closed. Press Pressure Cook and select High Pressure; set cooking time for 3 minutes. When time is up, press Cancel to turn off pot. Allow pressure to naturally release for 10 minutes. Move steam-release valve to Venting position and release remaining pressure. Remove lid and stir once.

**2** Just before serving, shred remaining apple on coarse side of box grater into bowl. Stir in labneh and maple syrup. Divide oats evenly among 6 bowls; top with labneh mixture and sprinkle with walnuts and nutmeg.

**Per serving** (scant 1 cup oats, ¼ cup labneh mixture, and ½ tablespoon walnuts): 267 Cal, 9 g Total Fat, 3 g Sat Fat, 208 mg Sod, 42 g Total Carb, 19 g Sugar, 6 g Fib, 6 g Prot.

## Smart pointers

Set out the oats and labneh as part of a brunch spread on the weekend. Serve a salad of orange and grapefruit segments mixed with sliced fresh strawberries and raspberries alongside for 0 additional SmartPoints®.

# Cranberry-almond morning barley

**Prep 2 min  Cook 10 min  Serves 4**

9 9 4

Tangy dried cranberries and crunchy sliced almonds play nicely against the creamy texture of cooked whole-grain barley. We opted for quick-cooking barley, which is done in about 10 minutes, so this dish can come together in a hurry.

- **2 tablespoons slivered or sliced almonds**
- **2 cups water**
- **1 cup quick-cooking barley**
- **⅓ cup dried cranberries**
- **Pinch salt**
- **¼ cup half-and-half**
- **½ teaspoon cinnamon**

**1** Put almonds in small skillet and set over medium-high heat. Cook, shaking pan frequently, until golden, about 2 minutes. Transfer almonds to small plate or cup.

**2** Meanwhile, bring water to boil in medium saucepan. Stir in barley, cranberries, and salt; reduce heat and simmer, covered, until water is absorbed and barley is tender, 10–12 minutes. Remove saucepan from heat and stir in half-and-half and cinnamon. Let stand, covered, 5 minutes. Divide evenly among 4 bowls and sprinkle with almonds.

**Per serving** (generous ¾ cup barley mixture and ½ tablespoon almonds): 254 Cal, 4 g Total Fat, 1 g Sat Fat, 90 mg Sod, 51 g Total Carb, 11 g Sugar, 9 g Fib, 6 g Prot.

## Serving idea

Top each serving of barley with 2 tablespoons of toasted unsweetened coconut flakes, if you'd like.

# Fruit-and-nut granola

**Prep 2 min Cook 20 min Serves 10**

5 5 4

Store-bought granola is no match for homemade. A batch is easy to whip up, and it's generally lower in both added fat and sugar. You can double the recipe and store leftovers in an airtight container for up to 2 weeks.

**1½ cups old-fashioned (rolled) oats**
**½ cup unprocessed wheat bran**
**¾ cup sliced almonds**
**¼ cup honey**
**½ teaspoon cinnamon**
**Pinch salt**
**⅓ cup golden raisins**
**¼ cup toasted wheat germ**

1 Preheat oven to 350°F.

2 Spread oats and bran on large rimmed baking sheet. Bake, stirring often, until lightly browned, about 10 minutes.

3 Meanwhile, stir together almonds, honey, cinnamon, and salt in large bowl. Add oat mixture and stir to combine. Spread mixture on baking sheet and bake, stirring often, until mixture is dark golden brown, about 10 minutes.

4 Transfer to bowl. Stir in raisins and wheat germ. Let cool completely before storing in airtight container.

**Per serving** (about ⅓ cup): 142 Cal, 5 g Total Fat, 0 g Sat Fat, 30 mg Sod, 24 g Total Carb, 11 g Sugar, 4 g Fib, 4 g Prot.

## Smart pointers

For a filling and healthy breakfast, enjoy the granola with your favorite fresh cut fruit or berries for 0 additional SmartPoints®.

# Yogurt breakfast parfaits

**Prep 12 min   Cook 0 min   Serves 6**

6 3 3

These parfaits make a great brown-bag breakfast. Layer a serving into a 1-cup mason jar, cover, and refrigerate until you're ready to leave for the day.

- **1 (32-ounce) container plain fat-free yogurt**
- **⅓ cup strawberry jam or preserves**
- **4 navel oranges**
- **2 bananas, thinly sliced**
- **⅓ cup nutlike cereal nuggets**

**1** Stir together yogurt and jam in medium bowl until blended.

**2** With small knife, cut away peel and pith from oranges. Working over another medium bowl, cut between membranes to release segments, allowing them to fall into bowl. Gently stir in bananas.

**3** Spoon about ⅓ cup of fruit mixture into each of 6 parfait glasses; top each with about ⅓ cup of yogurt mixture. Repeat layering once. Sprinkle each parfait with scant 1 tablespoon cereal.

**Per serving** (1 parfait): 232 Cal, 1 g Total Fat, 0 g Sat Fat, 160 mg Sod, 48 g Total Carb, 33 g Sugar, 4 g Fib, 11 g Prot.

## Try this

Change up the fruit according to what's in season—quartered strawberries in the spring, peach wedges or blueberries in the summer, chopped apple or pear tossed with lemon juice in the fall, or Ruby Red grapefruit in the winter.

# Canadian bacon, herb, and ricotta frittata

**Prep 10 min   Cook 18 min   Serves 4**

We like basil and parsley in this easy, aromatic frittata, but you could use other combinations of herbs, like chives and dill or mint and cilantro. You can also sub in smaller quantities—about ½ teaspoon each—of more potent herbs like oregano, thyme, and tarragon.

- **2 teaspoons olive oil**
- **3 ounces sliced Canadian bacon, cut into thin strips**
- **5 large eggs**
- **¼ cup low-fat (1%) milk**
- **¼ teaspoon + ⅛ teaspoon salt**
- **¼ teaspoon black pepper, plus more for garnish**
- **⅓ cup coarsely chopped fresh basil leaves**
- **⅓ cup coarsely chopped fresh parsley leaves**
- **½ cup part-skim ricotta**
- **2 tablespoons grated Parmesan**
- **Fresh basil leaves (optional)**

**1** Place oven rack in top third of oven and preheat to 400°F.

**2** Heat 1 teaspoon oil in 9-inch ovenproof skillet over medium heat. Add bacon and cook until browned, about 2 minutes. With slotted spoon, transfer to plate.

**3** Beat eggs, milk, salt, and pepper in medium bowl until combined. Stir in bacon, basil, and parsley. Return skillet to medium heat and add remaining 1 teaspoon oil. Pour in egg mixture. Dot ricotta evenly over eggs and sprinkle with Parmesan. Cook, lifting up edge of frittata occasionally and allowing eggs to flow underneath, until eggs are set around edge, about 4 minutes.

**4** Transfer skillet to oven and bake until frittata is set in middle and top is browned in spots, about 10 minutes. (You can run the frittata under the broiler briefly for browner top.) Let frittata cool 5 minutes. Sprinkle with additional pepper and basil leaves, if using, and cut into 4 wedges.

**Per serving** (1 wedge): 198 Cal, 12 g Total Fat, 5 g Sat Fat, 561 mg Sod, 4 g Total Carb, 1 g Sugar, 0 g Fib, 17 g Prot.

## Serving idea

Toast whole-wheat or whole-grain English muffins and serve half of one alongside each slice of frittata.

# Steak and egg burritos

**Prep 25 min  Cook 8 min  Serves 4**

9 7 7

Breakfast burritos are a hearty, portable meal that is easy to eat on the go. This version is great if you have leftover steak, or you can use lean store-bought roast beef from the deli counter.

- **6 large egg whites**
- **4 large eggs**
- **½ red bell pepper, chopped**
- **2 scallions, sliced**
- **¾ cup fat-free salsa**
- **1 tablespoon chopped fresh cilantro**
- **½ teaspoon paprika**
- **¼ teaspoon black pepper**
- **1 teaspoon canola oil**
- **4 (8-inch) whole-wheat tortillas**
- **1 cup baby spinach leaves**
- **1 (6-ounce) piece lean cooked sirloin or sirloin roast beef, trimmed and cut into bite-size pieces**
- **4 tablespoons shredded reduced-fat Monterey Jack**

1 Preheat oven to 400°F. Spray small rimmed baking sheet with nonstick spray.

2 Meanwhile, beat egg whites and eggs in large bowl. Stir in bell pepper, scallions, ¼ cup salsa, cilantro, paprika, and black pepper.

3 Heat oil in large nonstick skillet set over medium heat. Add egg mixture and cook until eggs begin to set, about 1½ minutes; push egg mixture toward center of skillet to form large soft curds, cooking until eggs are just set, about 2 minutes longer.

4 Lay tortillas on work surface. Top with one fourth of spinach. Spoon one fourth of egg mixture along center of each tortilla; top with one fourth beef and 1 tablespoon Monterey Jack. Fold top and bottom edges of tortillas over, then roll up to enclose filling. Place, seam side down, on prepared baking sheet.

5 Bake until burritos are heated through and cheese is melted, about 5 minutes. Serve with remaining ½ cup salsa.

**Per serving** (1 burrito with 2 tablespoons salsa): 344 Cal, 14 g Total Fat, 6 g Sat Fat, 1,027 mg Sod, 24 g Total Carb, 4 g Sugar, 5 g Fib, 29 g Prot.

## Prep ahead

You can make the burritos the night before: Cover with plastic wrap and refrigerate. To reheat, remove plastic, wrap loosely in a paper towel, and microwave on High until heated throughout, 1 to 2 minutes.

# Spanish-style potato tortilla

**Prep 10 min  Cook 20 min  Serves 6**

5 3 1

This popular tapas dish is great for a crowd, reheats well, and is loaded with SmartPoints®-friendly potatoes. Instead of frying the potatoes as classic recipes do, we keep things lean by cooking them in a nonstick skillet with very little oil.

- **3 baking potatoes (8–10 ounces each), peeled and thinly sliced**
- **3 large eggs**
- **3 large egg whites**
- **½ teaspoon salt**
- **¼ teaspoon black pepper**
- **1½ tablespoons canola oil**
- **1 medium onion, chopped**
- **½ red bell pepper, thinly sliced**

**1** Put potatoes in large saucepan with enough cold water to cover; bring to boil over high heat. Reduce heat and cook until potatoes are half-cooked, about 5 minutes. Drain and set aside.

**2** Meanwhile, beat eggs, egg whites, salt, and black pepper in large bowl.

**3** Heat oil in 10-inch heavy nonstick skillet over medium-high heat. Add potatoes, onion, and bell pepper and cook, stirring occasionally, until potatoes are golden brown, about 5 minutes. Add potato mixture to beaten eggs, stirring until mixed well.

**4** Reduce heat to medium-low. Pour potato-egg mixture into same skillet and cook, without stirring, 2 minutes. Remove skillet from heat. Place large plate on top of skillet. Wearing oven mitts (skillet will be hot), turn skillet with plate over to invert tortilla. Lift off skillet and slide tortilla back into skillet. Cook until eggs are set, about 2 minutes longer. Cut tortilla into 6 wedges.

**Per serving** (1 wedge): 167 Cal, 6 g Total Fat, 1 g Sat Fat, 259 mg Sod, 21 g Total Carb, 2 g Sugar, 3 g Fib, 7 g Prot.

## Smart pointers

Serving a wedge of this egg-and-potato classic with slices of juicy tomato and sweet onion topped with fresh parsley is a great way to get your first dose of veggies for the day.

# Veggie omelette sandwiches

**Prep 10 min Cook 13 min Serves 4**

These breakfast sandwiches are excellent for a sit-down or grab-and-go meal. You can chop the onion and bell pepper and slice up the mushrooms the night before and store in the fridge to save time. You can prep the eggs through step 1 and refrigerate those as well.

- **6 large eggs**
- **2 tablespoons chopped fresh flat-leaf parsley**
- **½ teaspoon salt**
- **¼ teaspoon black pepper**
- **1½ teaspoons canola oil**
- **1 medium onion, finely chopped**
- **1 green bell pepper, chopped**
- **1 cup sliced white mushrooms**
- **4 whole-wheat English muffins, split and toasted**
- **4 thick tomato slices**

**1** Beat eggs, parsley, salt, and black pepper in medium bowl.

**2** Coat medium nonstick skillet with ½ teaspoon oil and set over medium heat. Add onion, bell pepper, and mushrooms and cook, stirring occasionally, until vegetables are softened, about 5 minutes. Transfer to clean medium bowl.

**3** Wipe skillet clean with paper towels. Coat skillet with ½ teaspoon oil and set over medium heat; pour in half of egg mixture. Cook, lifting edge of eggs frequently with spatula to allow uncooked portion of egg to run underneath, until eggs are not quite set, about 3 minutes.

**4** Spoon half of vegetable mixture over one half of eggs. With spatula, fold unfilled portion of eggs over to enclose filling. Reduce heat to low and cook until eggs are set, about 1 minute longer.

**5** Slide omelette onto plate and cover to keep warm. Repeat with remaining ½ teaspoon oil, eggs, and vegetable mixture to make 1 more omelette. Cut each omelette in half. Place one slice of tomato on bottom of each English muffin and top with one portion of omelette. Cover with tops of English muffins.

**Per serving** (1 sandwich): 277 Cal, 10 g Total Fat, 3 g Sat Fat, 644 mg Sod, 31 g Total Carb, 5 g Sugar, 3 g Fib, 15 g Prot.

## Serving idea

Top each slice of tomato with ¼ of a sliced Hass avocado.

# Five-cheese spinach quiche

**Prep 15 min   Cook 30 min   Serves 6**

7 5 5

Crustless quiches are easy to put together and low in SmartPoints®, so you can double down on mouthwatering fillings (like five cheeses!).

- **1 teaspoon olive oil**
- **1 small onion, diced**
- **5 large eggs**
- **¼ cup low-fat (1%) milk**
- **1½ teaspoons Dijon mustard**
- **1 teaspoon dried oregano**
- **½ teaspoon salt**
- **¼ teaspoon black pepper**
- **8 ounces frozen chopped spinach, thawed and squeezed dry**
- **1 cup part-skim ricotta**
- **¾ cup shredded reduced-fat cheddar**
- **2 ounces soft goat cheese, crumbled**
- **¼ cup crumbled Gorgonzola or other blue cheese**
- **2 tablespoons grated Parmesan**

**1** Preheat oven to 375°F. Spray 9-inch pie plate with nonstick spray.

**2** Heat oil in large skillet over medium heat. Add onion and cook, stirring occasionally, until softened, about 5 minutes. Let cool.

**3** Whisk eggs, milk, mustard, oregano, salt, and pepper in large bowl; stir in spinach. Stir in ricotta, cheddar, goat cheese, Gorgonzola, and onion. Spoon into prepared pie plate, spreading evenly; sprinkle with Parmesan.

**4** Bake until quiche is just set and knife inserted into center comes out clean, about 25 minutes. Let cool 10 minutes. Cut into 6 wedges.

**Per serving** (1 wedge): 221 Cal, 13 g Total Fat, 7 g Sat Fat, 626 mg Sod, 6 g Total Carb, 2 g Sugar, 1 g Fib, 18 g Prot.

## Prep ahead

You can prepare the mixture of onion, eggs, milk, seasonings, and cheeses several hours ahead or the night before: Cover and refrigerate, but leave it out at room temperature about 30 minutes before cooking so it can warm up enough to keep the baking time the same.

# Lox and eggs bagel sandwiches

**Prep 10 min Cook 5 min Serves 4**

9 6 6

Lox, eggs, and bagels are practically a Sunday morning institution. Bagel thins keep the SmartPoints® low while shallots, dill, and chives punch up the flavor.

- **6 tablespoons light cream cheese (Neufchâtel), softened**
- **2 shallots, minced**
- **4 teaspoons chopped fresh dill, plus additional for garnish**
- **1 tablespoon finely chopped fresh chives, plus additional for garnish**
- **¼ teaspoon black pepper**
- **4 large eggs**
- **2 teaspoons canola oil**
- **4 everything bagel thins, toasted**
- **1 (4-ounce) package sliced lox or smoked salmon**

1 Mix together 2 tablespoons cream cheese, shallots, dill, chives, and pepper in medium bowl until blended. Stir in eggs until mixed well.

2 Heat oil in large nonstick skillet over medium heat. Add egg mixture and cook, without stirring, until eggs begin to set, about 1 minute. Cook, pushing egg mixture toward center of skillet to form large soft curds, until just set, about 3 minutes longer. Remove skillet from heat.

3 Spread remaining ¼ cup cream cheese on bottoms of bagel thins; top evenly with eggs and smoked salmon. Garnish with dill and chives. Cover with tops of bagel thins.

**Per serving** (1 sandwich): 288 Cal, 13 g Total Fat, 4 g Sat Fat, 934 mg Sod, 28 g Total Carb, 5 g Sugar, 5 g Fib, 18 g Prot.

# Fluffy lemon-ricotta pancakes

**Prep 20 min  Cook 10 min  Serves 6**

Creamy ricotta cheese and beaten egg whites ensure that these lemony pancakes are rich yet light. Make a double batch and freeze to enjoy at another time. Defrost them in your microwave or overnight in the fridge.

**1½ cups all-purpose flour**
**1 teaspoon baking soda**
**½ teaspoon salt**
**1 cup low-fat buttermilk**
**½ cup part-skim ricotta**
**2 large eggs, yolks and whites separated and at room temperature**
**2 tablespoons sugar**
**2 tablespoons grated lemon zest, plus lemon peel strips for garnish**
**2 teaspoons canola oil**

**1** Set baking sheet on middle rack in oven and preheat to 200°F.

**2** Whisk together flour, baking soda, and salt in small bowl. Stir together buttermilk, ricotta, egg yolks, sugar, and lemon zest in medium bowl until blended.

**3** With electric mixer on medium speed, beat egg whites in another medium bowl until soft peaks form when beaters are lifted. With rubber spatula, gently stir flour mixture into buttermilk mixture just until flour mixture is moistened. Fold in beaten whites in two additions just until no white streaks remain.

**4** Brush oil on large nonstick griddle and set over medium heat (if using electric griddle, preheat to 375°F). Pour ¼ cupfuls of batter onto griddle, spacing evenly, and cook until bubbles appear along edge and pancakes are lightly browned, about 3 minutes. Turn pancakes over and cook until lightly browned on second side, 2–3 minutes longer, transferring pancakes to baking sheet in oven as they are done. Repeat, making total of 12 pancakes. Serve sprinkled with lemon peel strips.

**Per serving** (2 pancakes): 213 Cal, 5 g Total Fat, 2 g Sat Fat, 509 mg Sod, 31 g Total Carb, 6 g Sugar, 1 g Fib, 9 g Prot.

## Smart pointers

These pancakes are tasty and satisfying just as they are, but you can also top them with mixed fresh berries, sliced banana, or fat-free Greek yogurt, along with a dusting (¼ teaspoon per serving) of confectioners' sugar for 0 SmartPoints®.

# French toast with strawberry sauce

**Prep 10 min Cook 8 min Serves 4**

9 7 7

To make life easy, you can cook this French toast before everyone shows up for breakfast. Place a wire rack over a baking sheet and set in a 200°F oven. As batches are done, place them on the rack; keep warm up to 30 minutes. If you've got fresh berries, serve them along with the sauce.

- **2 cups frozen unsweetened strawberries, very coarsely chopped**
- **¼ cup water**
- **1 tablespoon sugar**
- **4 large eggs**
- **¾ cup low-fat (1%) milk**
- **1 teaspoon vanilla extract**
- **¼ teaspoon cinnamon**
- **8 slices whole-wheat or multigrain bread**
- **2 teaspoons canola oil**

**1** To make sauce, combine strawberries and water in small saucepan and set over low heat. Cook, stirring occasionally, until berries are thawed and saucy, about 2 minutes. Remove saucepan from heat and stir in sugar until dissolved. Set aside.

**2** To make French toast, beat eggs, milk, vanilla, and cinnamon in large shallow bowl. Dip bread, one slice at a time, into egg mixture until well coated on both sides.

**3** Brush oil on griddle or in very large nonstick skillet and set over medium heat. Cook French toast, in batches, until deep golden, about 2 minutes per side, transferring to plate as it is done, covering to keep warm. Place 2 pieces of French toast on each of 4 plates and spoon sauce on top.

**Per serving** (2 slices French toast and about ¼ cup sauce): 315 Cal, 10 g Total Fat, 2 g Sat Fat, 385 mg Sod, 40 g Total Carb, 12 g Sugar, 5 g Fib, 16 g Prot.

## Smart pointers

**Double the strawberry sauce and put extras in the fridge to layer with plain fat-free Greek yogurt for easy breakfast parfaits.**

# Eat-your-greens breakfast muffins

**Prep 20 min Cook 20 min Serves 12**

We packed these muffins with lots of good-for-you ingredients to kickstart your morning: yogurt, banana, kale, and matcha powder (finely ground green tea). Don't forget the paper liners for no sticking worries and grab-and-go simplicity.

- **1 cup white whole-wheat flour**
- **1 cup all-purpose flour**
- **⅓ cup sugar**
- **1½ tablespoons matcha powder (optional)**
- **2 teaspoons baking powder**
- **1 teaspoon cinnamon**
- **½ teaspoon baking soda**
- **½ teaspoon salt**
- **⅔ cup plain fat-free yogurt**
- **¼ cup canola oil**
- **2 ripe bananas, thickly sliced**
- **1 (5-ounce) container baby kale**
- **1 large egg**
- **1½ teaspoons vanilla extract**

**1** Preheat oven to 350°F. Line 12-cup muffin pan with paper liners.

**2** Whisk together whole-wheat flour, all-purpose flour, sugar, matcha powder, if using, baking powder, cinnamon, baking soda, and salt in large bowl.

**3** Combine yogurt, oil, and bananas in blender and puree. Add kale in batches and puree. Add egg and vanilla and pulse just until combined. Add yogurt mixture to flour mixture, stirring until flour mixture is just moistened. Spoon batter evenly into lined muffin cups. Bake until toothpick inserted in center of muffin comes out clean, about 20 minutes.

**4** Let muffins cool in pan on wire rack 5 minutes. Remove muffins from pan and place on rack. Serve warm or at room temperature.

**Per serving** (1 muffin): 182 Cal, 5 g Total Fat, 1 g Sat Fat, 253 mg Sod, 29 g Total Carb, 10 g Sugar, 3 g Fib, 4 g Prot.

## Shopping tip

Look for matcha at health-food stores and Asian markets or order it online.

Chapter 2

# Lunch

# Salad made easy | Recipe builder

START WITH THE BASE

## Perfectly dressed green salad

**Prep 5 min Cook 0 min Serves 1**

Whisk together **1 teaspoon extra-virgin olive oil, 1 teaspoon water, 1 teaspoon white wine vinegar,** and **⅛ teaspoon salt** in serving bowl. Add **3 cups mixed salad greens, such as romaine, green or red leaf lettuce, baby spinach, baby arugula or baby kale, Boston or butter lettuce, frisee and/or gem lettuce,** rinsed. Toss gently until salad is evenly coated.

BUILD YOUR BOWL

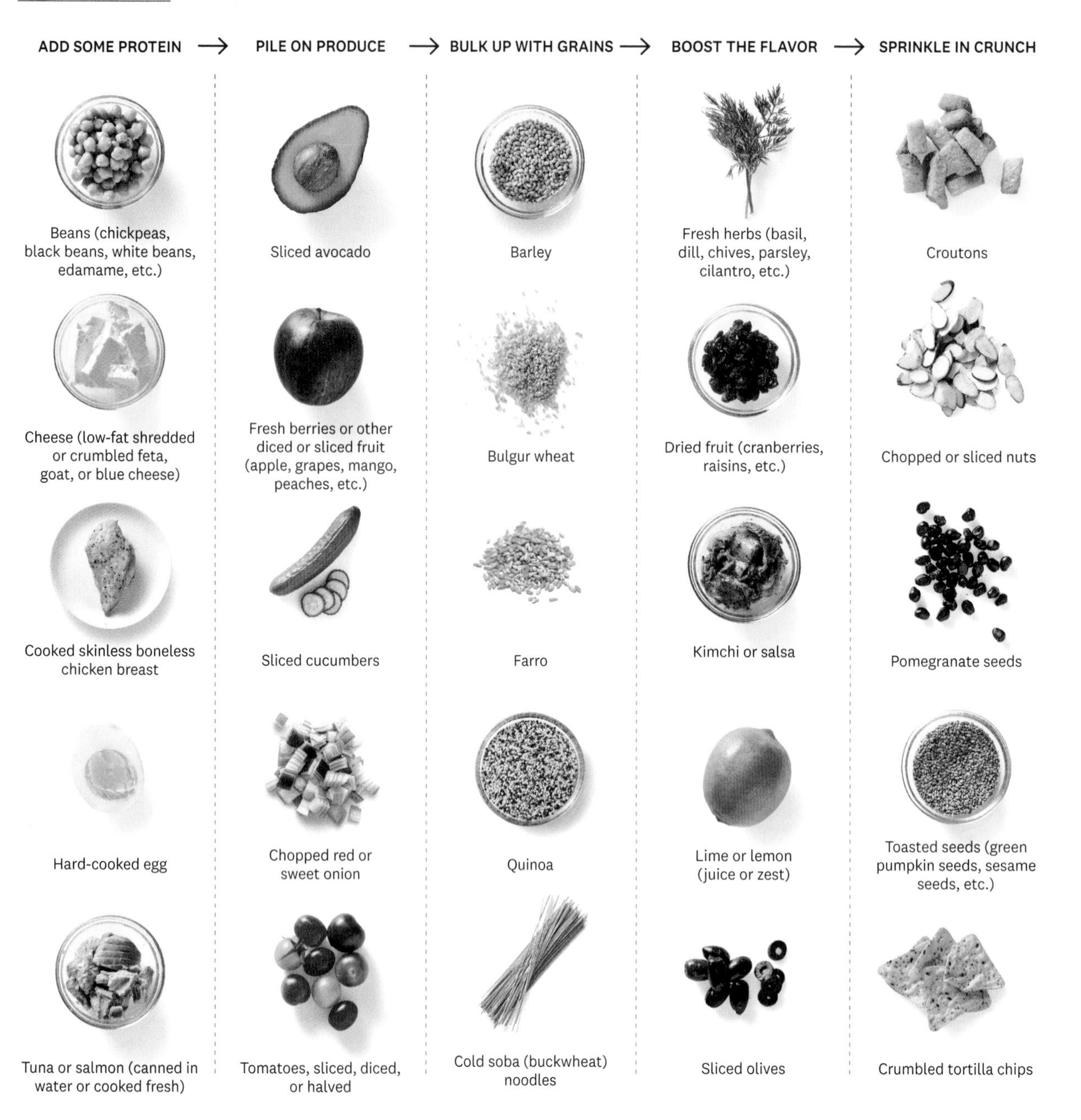

# Some toppings we love

### Asian chicken and soba

6 4 4

½ cup diced cooked skinless chicken breast + ¼ avocado + 2 tablespoons sliced red onion + ⅓ cup cooked soba noodles + ¼ cup sliced kimchi + 1 teaspoon toasted sesame seeds

### Southwest with mango

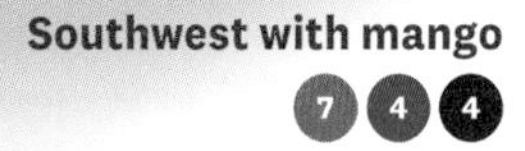


½ cup rinsed and drained canned black beans + ¼ cup diced fresh mango + ¼ sliced avocado + ¼ cup pico de gallo or fat-free salsa + lime juice + 3 crumbled baked tortilla chips

### California salmon with quinoa

1 (3.75-ounce) can drained flaked red salmon + ½ cup sliced cucumber + ⅓ cup cooked quinoa + 2 tablespoons chopped fresh dill + 1 tablespoon toasted sliced almonds

START WITH THE BASE

## Easy soup base

**Prep 5 min Cook 25 min Serves 4**

- **1 teaspoon olive oil**
- **½ small onion, diced**
- **1 garlic clove, crushed with side of knife**
- **4 cups (32 ounces) store-bought or homemade chicken or vegetable broth**
- **Bay leaf (optional)**
- **Salt and freshly ground pepper to taste**

Heat oil in medium saucepan over medium heat. Add onion and garlic and cook, stirring, until onion softens, about 3 minutes. Add broth and bay leaf (if using). Bring to boil over high heat. Reduce heat and simmer a few minutes. Discard bay leaf. Season to taste lightly with salt and pepper. Broth can be refrigerated up to 3 days or frozen for several months. Makes 4 cups.
Per serving: 1 cup

VARIATIONS TO TRY:

## Edamame egg drop soup

**Prep 3 min Cook 10 min Serves 1**

Bring **1 cup Easy soup base** to boil in small saucepan. Add **⅓ cup frozen shelled edamame** and cook until tender, about 5 minutes. Meanwhile, whisk together **1½ teaspoons cornstarch** and **1 tablespoon cold water** in cup until smooth. Reduce heat so broth simmers. Slowly whisk cornstarch mixture into broth; simmer until thickened, about 1 minute. Slowly drizzle **1 beaten large egg** into broth while stirring in circular motion. Cook 1 minute. Pour into bowl and sprinkle with **thinly sliced scallion and radish** and serve with **soy sauce,** if desired.

## Tomato-fennel soup

**Prep 3 min Cook 17 min Serves 1**

Heat **1 teaspoon olive oil** in small saucepan over medium heat. Add **½ diced small fennel bulb** and **1 diced shallot.** Cook, stirring, until softened, about 5 minutes. Add **¾ cup Easy soup base** and **¾ cup canned diced tomatoes;** bring to boil. Reduce heat and simmer until vegetables are very tender, about 10 minutes. Pour into bowl and top with **2 tablespoons plain fat-free Greek yogurt;** sprinkle with **fennel fronds,** if desired.

## Ramen soup with tofu

**Prep 3 min Cook 10 min Serves 1**

Bring **2 cups Easy soup base** and **½ cup sliced shiitake mushroom caps** to boil in medium saucepan. Reduce heat and simmer until mushrooms are tender, about 5 minutes. Stir in **1 teaspoon chopped fresh ginger.** Add **1½ ounces (½ block) ramen noodles** and **4 ounces smoked or baked tofu;** simmer until noodles soften, about 3 minutes. Pour into bowl and sprinkle with **1 thinly sliced scallion.** Serve with **soy sauce,** if desired.

### Edamame egg drop soup

### Tomato-fennel soup

### Ramen soup with tofu

# Southwestern chicken soup

**Prep 12 min  Cook 22 min  Serves 4**

6 3 3

Classic Tex-Mex ingredients—including jalapeño, lime, corn, and avocado—give this soup bold flavor without a lot of fuss. Cutting the chicken breast into small bite-size pieces cuts down on cooking time.

- **2 teaspoons olive oil**
- **1 pound skinless boneless chicken breasts, cut into ½-inch pieces**
- **½ teaspoon salt**
- **¼ teaspoon black pepper**
- **1 medium onion, chopped**
- **1 small green bell pepper, chopped**
- **1 jalapeño pepper, seeded and minced**
- **2 garlic cloves, minced**
- **1 tablespoon chili powder**
- **2 teaspoons ground cumin**
- **2 (14½-ounce) cans reduced-sodium chicken broth**
- **1 (14½-ounce) can diced tomatoes, drained**
- **1 cup fresh or frozen corn kernels**
- **1 tablespoon lime juice**
- **½ Hass avocado, pitted, peeled, and cut into 8 slices**
- **¼ cup lightly packed fresh cilantro leaves**

**1** Heat 1 teaspoon oil in Dutch oven over medium-high heat. Sprinkle chicken with salt and black pepper. Add chicken to pot and cook, stirring often, until lightly browned and cooked through, about 5 minutes. Transfer to plate.

**2** Add remaining 1 teaspoon oil to pot. Add onion, bell pepper, and jalapeño and cook, stirring often, until vegetables are softened, about 3 minutes. Add garlic, chili powder, and cumin and cook, stirring constantly, until fragrant, about 30 seconds longer. Stir in broth, tomatoes, and corn. Cover and bring to boil.

**3** Reduce heat to low and simmer, covered, until vegetables are tender, about 8 minutes. Stir in chicken and cook just until heated through, about 2 minutes longer. Remove from heat and stir in lime juice.

**4** Ladle soup evenly into 4 bowls. Top each serving with 2 slices avocado and sprinkle with cilantro.

**Per serving** (1¾ cups soup and 2 slices avocado): 291 Cal, 10 g Total Fat, 2 g Sat Fat, 1,017 mg Sod, 23 g Total Carb, 7 g Sugar, 6 g Fib, 31 g Prot.

## Serving idea

Top each bowl with 3 crumbled, baked corn tortilla chips.

# Mushroom-barley soup with red miso

**Prep 12 min  Cook 37 min  Serves 6**

4 4 2

This is not your grandma's barley soup: Our veggie-packed, Asian-inspired version features an intriguing mix of colors and flavors for a soul-satisfying meal in a bowl. Red miso is a particularly deep-flavored type of miso, but you can substitute milder white or yellow varieties if you prefer.

- **1 ounce dried shiitake mushrooms**
- **2 cups boiling water**
- **1 tablespoon canola oil**
- **3 carrots, sliced**
- **1 medium onion, finely chopped**
- **3 garlic cloves, minced**
- **1 tablespoon grated peeled fresh ginger**
- **⅔ cup pearl barley**
- **6 cups mushroom or vegetable broth**
- **½ pound bok choy, halved lengthwise and cut into ½-inch slices**
- **3 tablespoons red miso**
- **1 tablespoon lemon juice**
- **4 scallions (dark-green parts only), sliced**

**1** Place mushrooms in large glass measure or bowl and add boiling water. Let soak until mushrooms are softened, about 20 minutes. With slotted spoon, lift mushrooms out of water; reserve liquid. Chop mushrooms.

**2** Meanwhile, heat oil in Dutch oven over medium heat. Add carrots and onion; cook, stirring occasionally, until vegetables are softened, about 5 minutes. Add garlic and ginger and cook, stirring constantly, just until fragrant, about 30 seconds longer.

**3** Stir barley and mushrooms into Dutch oven; pour in reserved mushroom liquid, pouring carefully so that any grit in bottom of cup is left behind. Stir in broth and bring to boil over high heat. Reduce heat and simmer, covered, until barley is tender, about 30 minutes. Stir in bok choy and simmer until crisp-tender, about 2 minutes longer.

**4** Whisk together miso and 1 cup hot broth from pot in small bowl until smooth. Stir into soup along with lemon juice. Serve sprinkled with scallions.

**Per serving** (about 1½ cups): 175 Cal, 3 g Total Fat, 0 g Sat Fat, 925 mg Sod, 33 g Total Carb, 5 g Sugar, 7 g Fib, 5 g Prot.

## Shopping tip

Mushroom broth is a flavorful option for making vegan and vegetarian soups. Look for it in larger supermarkets and health-food stores.

# Turkey meatball and escarole soup

**Prep 35 min  Cook 4 hrs  Serves 8**

4 2 2

Soaking torn bread in milk before adding it to the turkey mixture ensures the meatballs stay moist and tender after hours in the slow cooker, while Parmesan adds a touch of classic Italian flavor. Mix lightly and shape the meatballs gently to keep them from becoming too dense.

- **2 slices whole-wheat bread, crusts removed and cut into ½-inch pieces**
- **¼ cup low-fat (1%) milk**
- **1 (1¼-pound) package ground skinless turkey breast**
- **¼ cup grated Parmesan**
- **1 large egg, lightly beaten**
- **1 large shallot, minced**
- **3 tablespoons chopped fresh flat-leaf parsley**
- **1 teaspoon salt**
- **½ teaspoon black pepper**
- **1 tablespoon olive oil**
- **2 (32-ounce) cartons reduced-sodium chicken broth**
- **4 cups lightly packed thinly sliced escarole, Swiss chard, or kale**
- **1 (15½-ounce) can cannellini (white kidney) beans, rinsed and drained**

**1** Mix together bread and milk in large bowl; let stand until softened, about 5 minutes. Add turkey, Parmesan, egg, shallot, 2 tablespoons parsley, salt, and pepper, stirring until mixed well but not overmixed.

**2** With damp hands, shape turkey mixture into 24 meatballs, using about 2 tablespoons for each meatball; transfer meatballs to sheet of foil as they are shaped. Wash bowl.

**3** Heat oil in large heavy nonstick skillet over medium-high heat. Add meatballs, in two batches, and cook until well browned, about 5 minutes per batch. Transfer meatballs to cleaned bowl as they are browned.

**4** Combine broth, escarole, and beans in 5- or 6-quart slow cooker; add meatballs. Cover and cook until meatballs are cooked through, about 4 hours on Low. Serve soup sprinkled with remaining 1 tablespoon parsley.

**Per serving** (1⅓ cups soup and 3 meatballs): 202 Cal, 5 g Total Fat, 1 g Sat Fat, 1,035 mg Sod, 15 g Total Carb, 2 g Sugar, 3 g Fib, 25 g Prot.

## Smart pointers

Add 1 cup of sliced white mushrooms or earthy cremini mushrooms to the soup along with the meatballs in step 4 for 0 SmartPoints®.

# Buffalo-style chicken salad

**Prep 15 min Cook 8 min Serves 4**

4 3 3

Our riff on Buffalo chicken wings has all the classic spiciness with only a fraction of the fat and calories of restaurant versions. Get ready for a hearty lunch salad that uses lean chicken tenders, blue cheese, and loads of crunchy vegetables.

- **½ teaspoon hot smoked paprika**
- **½ teaspoon ground cumin**
- **¼ teaspoon chili powder**
- **¾ teaspoon salt**
- **¼ teaspoon + ⅛ teaspoon black pepper**
- **12 chicken tenders (about 1 pound)**
- **1½ tablespoons extra-virgin olive oil**
- **2 tablespoons red-wine vinegar**
- **1 garlic clove, minced**
- **2 teaspoons hot pepper sauce, or to taste**
- **4 cups lightly packed sliced romaine lettuce**
- **1 Kirby cucumber, diced**
- **2 celery stalks, thinly sliced, and ⅓ cup lightly packed leaves, reserved**
- **2 scallions, thinly sliced**
- **1 red bell pepper, diced**
- **1 carrot, diced**
- **⅓ cup crumbled blue cheese**

**1** To make spice mix, stir together paprika, cumin, chili powder, ½ teaspoon salt, and ¼ teaspoon black pepper in cup. Evenly sprinkle on both sides of chicken tenders. Set aside.

**2** To make dressing, whisk together oil, vinegar, garlic, remaining ¼ teaspoon salt, and remaining ⅛ teaspoon black pepper in small bowl. Set aside.

**3** Spray ridged grill pan with nonstick spray and set over medium-high heat. Add chicken and grill until cooked through and well browned, about 4 minutes per side. Transfer to plate; drizzle with hot sauce, turning to coat.

**4** Put lettuce, cucumber, sliced celery, and scallions in large bowl; add dressing and toss until coated evenly. Divide lettuce mixture evenly among 4 plates or bowls; top with bell pepper, carrot, and chicken. Scatter celery leaves and blue cheese on top.

**Per serving** (3 chicken tenders, 2 cups salad, and generous 1 tablespoon cheese): 226 Cal, 9 g Total Fat, 3 g Sat Fat, 899 mg Sod, 7 g Total Carb, 3 g Sugar, 3 g Fib, 28 g Prot.

## Serving idea

Add a whole grain to the salad; try ½ cup cooked quinoa or farro.

# Chicken and bok choy bowls with sesame-ginger dressing

**Prep 20 min Cook 10 min Serves 4**

6 4 2

The Instant Pot® is a great tool for steam-cooking chicken breasts, as it locks in both nutrition and flavor. While you're at it, consider tossing one or two extra breasts into the pot; you can refrigerate or freeze them to have on hand for a quick lunch another day.

- **2 skinless boneless chicken breasts (about 1¼ pounds)**
- **4 baby bok choy (about 1 pound), halved lengthwise**
- **1 cup snow peas, trimmed and halved diagonally**
- **3 tablespoons water**
- **2 tablespoons rice vinegar**
- **1½ tablespoons white or yellow miso**
- **2 teaspoons Asian (dark) sesame oil**
- **1½ teaspoons honey**
- **1½ teaspoons grated peeled fresh ginger**
- **1 teaspoon soy sauce**
- **1 carrot, julienned or shredded**
- **1⅓ cups frozen cooked quinoa, prepared according to package directions**
- **2 teaspoons sesame seeds**

**1** Put steamer insert in 6-quart Instant Pot; add ¾ cup water. Arrange chicken on insert. Lock lid, making sure vent is closed.

**2** Press Pressure Cook and select High Pressure; set cooking time for 8 minutes. When time is up, press Cancel to turn off pot. Move steam-release valve to Venting position to quickly release pressure. Remove lid. Check chicken for doneness by piercing breast with tip of paring knife; it should show no trace of pink, and an instant-read thermometer inserted in center should register 165°F. If not cooked through, cover Instant Pot and lock lid; let chicken stand 5 minutes (chicken will continue to cook from residual heat). Transfer chicken to cutting board.

**3** Place bok choy and snow peas on insert in pot. Lock lid, making sure vent is closed. Press Pressure Cook and select High Pressure; set cooking time for 2 minutes. When time is up, press Cancel to turn off pot. Move steam-release valve to Venting position to quickly release pressure. Transfer vegetables to plate and let cool.

**4** Meanwhile, whisk together water, vinegar, miso, sesame oil, honey, ginger, and soy sauce in small bowl. Slice chicken lengthwise in half, then cut crosswise into strips. Arrange bok choy, chicken, carrot, snow peas, and quinoa in 4 bowls, dividing evenly. Drizzle with dressing and sprinkle with sesame seeds.

**Per serving** (1 bowl and 1½ tablespoons dressing): 328 Cal, 9 g Total Fat, 1 g Sat Fat, 490 mg Sod, 24 g Total Carb, 7 g Sugar, 5 g Fib, 39 g Prot.

# Salad Niçoise wraps

**Prep 12 min  Cook 14 min  Serves 4**

Cooking the potatoes and green beans for this salad in the same saucepan at the same time is a great time- and pot-saver. The green beans are cooked for only 4 minutes, which ensures they stay bright green and crisp-tender.

- **4 small red potatoes (about 1 pound total), scrubbed and quartered**
- **½ pound green beans, trimmed**
- **⅓ cup chicken broth**
- **2 tablespoons red-wine vinegar**
- **2 teaspoons Dijon mustard**
- **2 teaspoons extra-virgin olive oil**
- **⅛ teaspoon salt, or to taste**
- **⅛ teaspoon black pepper, or to taste**
- **4 Boston or red leaf lettuce leaves**
- **1 (6-ounce) can chunk white or light tuna packed in water, drained and coarsely flaked**
- **2 tablespoons nonpareil (tiny) capers, drained**
- **8 Niçoise olives, pitted and halved**

**1** Put potatoes in large saucepan and add enough water to cover by 2 inches; bring to boil over high heat. Reduce heat to medium and cook 4 minutes. Add green beans and cook until potatoes are fork-tender and beans are crisp-tender, about 4 minutes longer. Drain and transfer to large bowl.

**2** Meanwhile, to make dressing, whisk together broth, vinegar, mustard, oil, salt, and pepper in small bowl until blended. Add half of dressing to potato-bean mixture and toss until coated evenly.

**3** Place 1 lettuce leaf on each of 4 plates. Top each with one fourth of potato-bean mixture, one fourth of tuna, ½ tablespoon of capers, and 4 olive halves. Drizzle evenly with remaining dressing.

**Per serving** (1 wrap): 181 Cal, 4 g Total Fat, 1 g Sat Fat, 464 mg Sod, 24 g Total Carb, 3 g Sugar, 4 g Fib, 13 g Prot.

## Serving idea

Crusty whole-wheat dinner rolls are great alongside this salad. One (1¼-ounce) roll adds just a few SmartPoints® per serving.

# Farro and beet salad with fennel and feta

**Prep 15 min  Cook 1 hr 5 min  Serves 6**

4 4 2

Main-dish grain salads like this one are excellent to have in your cooking arsenal: They're easy, light, and delicious, and they hold up well for pack-along lunches or picnics. If you'd like, make a double batch of farro and freeze the extra to have on hand for another meal.

**¾ cup farro**
**3 cups water**
**1 teaspoon salt**
**2 tablespoons red-wine vinegar**
**1 tablespoon extra-virgin olive oil**
**¼ teaspoon black pepper**
**1 small fennel bulb, halved and thinly sliced**
**4 ounces plain baked tofu, diced**
**½ cup chopped fresh flat-leaf parsley**
**3 scallions, thinly sliced**
**1 (8-ounce) package ready-cooked beets, diced**
**6 tablespoons crumbled feta**
**Lemon wedges (optional)**

**1** Combine farro, water, and ½ teaspoon salt in medium saucepan. Bring to boil over high heat. Reduce heat and simmer, covered, until farro is tender, about 1 hour. Drain farro well and transfer to medium bowl. Let cool slightly.

**2** Meanwhile, to make dressing, whisk together vinegar, oil, remaining ½ teaspoon salt, and pepper in large bowl. Add fennel, tofu, parsley, and scallions and toss to mix. Add farro and toss again. Spoon farro mixture onto platter or divide evenly among 6 plates; top evenly with beets and feta. Serve with lemon wedges, if desired.

**Per serving** (1 cup salad and 1 tablespoon cheese): 172 Cal, 6 g Total Fat, 2 g Sat Fat, 554 mg Sod, 25 g Total Carb, 7 g Sugar, 5 g Fib, 8 g Prot.

## Smart pointers

Want more veggies in your salad? Add thinly sliced radishes for a peppery bite and extra crunch.

# Black rice salad with tofu and squash

**Prep 20 min  Cook 35 min  Serves 6**

6 5 2

Want an even heartier salad? Try adding a cup of drained, patted-dry chickpeas to one side of the pan when you roast the squash; roasting concentrates their flavor and crisps them up, so you get more crunch in this rice and kale salad.

**1 cup black rice**
**1¾ cups water**
**¾ teaspoon + pinch salt**
**1 pound packaged peeled and seeded butternut squash, cut into ¾-inch dice**
**1 teaspoon chopped fresh thyme**
**2 tablespoons olive oil**
**1½ tablespoons red-wine vinegar**
**1½ teaspoons honey**
**¼ teaspoon black pepper**
**1 small shallot, minced**
**1 bunch lacinato (dinosaur) kale, stems removed and leaves thinly sliced**
**6 ounces smoked or baked tofu, diced**
**6 tablespoons pomegranate seeds**

1 Combine rice, water, and pinch salt in small saucepan and bring to boil over high heat. Reduce heat and simmer, covered, until rice is tender, about 30 minutes. Remove pan from heat and let rice stand, covered, 5 minutes. Transfer to large bowl and let stand, tossing occasionally, until slightly cooled, about 15 minutes.

2 Meanwhile, preheat oven to 425°F. Line large rimmed baking sheet with foil; spray foil with nonstick spray.

3 Combine squash, thyme, and ¼ teaspoon salt on baking sheet. Spray with olive oil nonstick spray and toss to coat. Spread squash in even layer and spray again with nonstick spray. Roast until squash is lightly browned and tender, about 25 minutes, turning once halfway through roasting time.

4 To make dressing, whisk together oil, vinegar, honey, ½ teaspoon salt, and pepper in small bowl. Stir in shallot.

5 Add squash, kale, and tofu to rice; drizzle with dressing and toss to coat. Divide salad among 6 bowls. Top evenly with pomegranate seeds.

**Per serving** (1⅓ cups salad and 1 tablespoon pomegranate seeds): 247 Cal, 8 g Total Fat, 1 g Sat Fat, 373 mg Sod, 41 g Total Carb, 6 g Sugar, 7 g Fiber, 8 g Prot.

## Shopping tip

Buying precut butternut squash is a time-saver, but you can also peel and seed your own to save a little money; you'll want 2 cups diced squash for this recipe. A small 1½-pound squash will give you more than enough. Roast it all and save extras to fold into a frittata or omelette for breakfast.

# Salmon, white bean, and pasta salad

**Prep 15 min  Cook 15 min  Serves 4**

8 4 2

This is a reach-into-your pantry dish. No penne or fusilli? Use any pasta shape you have on hand. The same goes for the beans: red kidney, chickpeas, small white, and pinto beans work just as well. Sub tuna for the salmon if that's what you've got.

- **4 ounces chickpea pasta, such as rotini, penne, or fusilli**
- **⅓ cup reduced-sodium chicken broth**
- **¼ cup red-wine vinegar**
- **1½ tablespoons olive oil**
- **1 tablespoon grated lemon zest**
- **½ teaspoon salt**
- **½ teaspoon black pepper**
- **1 (15½-ounce) can cannellini (white kidney) beans, rinsed and drained**
- **2 (6-ounce) cans water-packed wild pink salmon, drained and flaked, large pieces of skin and bone removed**
- **1 (7-ounce) jar roasted red peppers (not oil-packed), drained and cut into 1-inch pieces**
- **½ cup chopped red onion**
- **⅓ cup fresh flat-leaf parsley leaves**
- **4 teaspoons capers, drained**

**1** Cook pasta according to package directions. Drain and rinse under cool running water. Drain again.

**2** Meanwhile, whisk together broth, vinegar, oil, lemon zest, salt, and black pepper in large bowl. Add pasta, beans, salmon, roasted peppers, onion, parsley, and capers and toss to combine.

**Per serving** (about 1½ cups): 368 Cal, 10 g Total Fat, 1 g Sat Fat, 1,218 mg Sod, 44 g Total Carb, 3 g Sugar, 7 g Fib, 27 g Prot.

# Chicken Parmesan sandwiches

**Prep 10 min   Cook 18 min   Serves 4**

Imagine tender chicken breasts coated with crisp Italian-style bread crumbs, covered with a blanket of tomato sauce, and topped with creamy, gooey mozzarella—all in a lighter format. Thanks to the air fryer, our rendition of chicken Parmesan is as quick and healthy as it is tasty.

**1 tablespoon + 1 teaspoon red-wine vinegar**
**1 tablespoon extra-virgin olive oil**
**1 tablespoon water**
**1 large garlic clove, crushed through a press**
**½ teaspoon salt, plus more for sprinkling**
**¼ teaspoon dried oregano**
**¼ teaspoon black pepper**
**6 tablespoons Italian-seasoned dried bread crumbs**
**4 (¼-pound) chicken breast cutlets**
**½ cup low-fat marinara sauce**
**¼ cup shredded part-skim mozzarella**
**¼ cup grated Parmesan**
**½ cup lightly packed baby arugula**
**4 (1-ounce) slices country-style whole-wheat or whole-grain bread, lightly toasted**
**Red pepper flakes (optional)**

**1** Whisk together vinegar, oil, water, garlic, ½ teaspoon salt, oregano, and pepper in large shallow bowl. Spread bread crumbs on sheet of wax paper. Dip one chicken breast in vinegar mixture, turning to coat; lightly coat on both sides with crumbs. Repeat with remaining cutlets. Lightly spray chicken with nonstick spray.

**2** Depending on air fryer settings, preheat to 360°F or 370°F for 3 minutes. Spray basket with nonstick spray and add 2 chicken cutlets. Air-fry until golden and crisp, 4–5 minutes. Lift out basket. Turn chicken over; spread 2 tablespoons marinara sauce on each cutlet. Sprinkle each with 1 tablespoon mozzarella and 1 tablespoon Parmesan.

**3** Air-fry until chicken is cooked through and crisp and mozzarella is melted, 2–3 minutes. Keep warm. Air-fry remaining cutlets with remaining marinara, mozzarella, and Parmesan.

**4** Place a few arugula leaves on each slice of toast and top each with a chicken cutlet. Sprinkle with salt and red pepper flakes, if using, and serve warm.

**Per serving** (1 open-face sandwich): 346 Cal, 12 g Total Fat, 3 g Sat Fat, 992 mg Sod, 24 g Total Carb, 3 g Sugar, 3 g Fib, 35 g Prot.

# Salmon, cucumber, and mint sandwiches

**Prep 20 min  Cook 0 min  Serves 4**

Removing the baguette's soft center lowers the SmartPoints® and makes space for the salmon filling. Don't discard the bread you pull out: Put it into a food processor and pulse until crumbs form, then freeze them. To use the crumbs, thaw and toast them in a dry skillet until crisp.

- **1 (6-ounce) can water-packed salmon, drained and skin removed**
- **1 Persian cucumber, diced**
- **¼ cup chopped red onion**
- **8 pitted Kalamata olives, chopped**
- **3 tablespoons plain fat-free Greek yogurt**
- **2 tablespoons chopped fresh mint**
- **Grated zest and juice of ½ large lime**
- **¼ teaspoon salt, or to taste**
- **¼ teaspoon sriracha, or to taste**
- **1 (8-ounce) whole-wheat baguette, split and bready center removed**
- **4 small red leaf lettuce leaves**
- **8 thick slices tomato**

**1** With fork, flake salmon into medium bowl. Stir in cucumber, onion, olives, yogurt, mint, lime zest and juice, salt, and sriracha.

**2** Line bottom of bread with lettuce and tomatoes. Spoon salmon mixture over and cover with top of bread. Cut into 4 equal portions.

**Per serving** (1 sandwich): 221 Cal, 4 g Total Fat, 1 g Sat Fat, 716 mg Sod, 32 g Total Carb, 4 g Sugar, 3 g Fib, 16 g Prot.

## Shopping tip

When buying Persian cucumbers, check that they are very firm with no soft spots. These flavorful, crunchy cucumbers can be stored in the crisper drawer about 4 days.

# Thai lobster rolls

**Prep 12 min  Cook 0 min  Serves 4**

Lobster rolls are the ultimate summertime treat, and this Asian take won't disappoint. You can often buy precooked meat, or ask at many large supermarkets and fish markets to have whole lobsters steamed for you. Four pounds of whole lobster will yield 1 pound of meat.

- **1 pound cooked lobster meat, cut into bite-size chunks**
- **¼ cup reduced-fat mayonnaise**
- **2 tablespoons chopped fresh cilantro + leaves for garnish**
- **2 tablespoons chopped fresh basil**
- **2 teaspoons grated lime zest**
- **2 tablespoons lime juice**
- **¼ teaspoon salt**
- **¼ teaspoon hot pepper sauce, or to taste**
- **4 whole-wheat hot dog buns, toasted**
- **3 radishes, thinly sliced**

Mix together lobster, mayonnaise, cilantro, basil, lime zest and juice, salt, and hot sauce in medium bowl. Divide evenly among buns. Top with radishes and sprinkle with cilantro leaves.

**Per serving** (1 lobster roll): 304 Cal, 8 g Total Fat, 1 g Sat Fat, 1,073 mg Sod, 27 g Total Carb, 4 g Sugar, 4 g Fib, 28 g Prot.

## Smart pointers

This riff on a classic New England–style lobster roll pairs well with a crunchy Thai-inspired slaw of shredded green cabbage, shredded carrot, chopped fresh cilantro, and sliced scallion, dressed with fresh lime juice, a squirt of sriracha, and a touch of salt for 0 SmartPoints®.

# Eggplant BLT sandwiches

**Prep 30 min Cook 15 min Serves 4**

7 7 7

Roasted strips of eggplant take on baconlike smokiness in this deliciously different sandwich. Coconut aminos—short for amino acids—is a liquid made from the sap of coconut palm flowers. It's similar to soy sauce but is soy-free and gluten-free. Find it at health-food stores.

- **2 tablespoons olive oil**
- **2 teaspoons coconut aminos or soy sauce**
- **¾ teaspoon smoked paprika**
- **⅛ teaspoon garlic powder**
- **⅛ teaspoon + pinch black pepper**
- **2 pinches salt**
- **1 small eggplant, about ½ pound**
- **1½ ripe Hass avocados**
- **1 teaspoon lemon juice**
- **4 (1-ounce) slices country-style bread, preferably round, toasted**
- **1 large tomato, cut into 8 slices**
- **8 small lettuce leaves**
- **¼ cup very thinly sliced red onion**

**1** Preheat oven to 425°F. Line large baking sheet with parchment paper.

**2** Stir together oil, coconut aminos, paprika, garlic powder, ⅛ teaspoon black pepper, and pinch salt in small bowl. With mandoline or vegetable slicer, slice eggplant into very thin lengthwise slices (if using a knife, cut eggplant crosswise into very thin rounds). You need 16 slices; save any leftover eggplant for another use.

**3** Arrange eggplant slices on prepared baking sheet in single layer; brush on one side with half of spiced oil. Turn slices over and brush on other side with remaining oil. Bake until slices are crisp and begin to char, 15–17 minutes. Slide eggplant with parchment onto work surface; let cool briefly (eggplant will get crisper).

**4** Meanwhile, peel and pit avocados. Roughly chop and put into small bowl; add lemon juice and pinch each salt and pepper. With fork, mash until fairly smooth.

**5** To assemble sandwiches, lay toasted bread on work surface. Top each with one fourth of mashed avocado, tomato, lettuce, onion, and eggplant.

**Per serving** (1 open-face sandwich): 264 Cal, 16 g Total Fat, 2 g Sat Fat, 464 mg Sod, 28 g Total Carb, 7 g Sugar, 8 g Fib, 5 g Prot.

WW

# Beef, mango, and cucumber wraps

**Prep 25 min  Cook 0 min  Serves 4**

Chili-garlic sauce adds complex heat to these lettuce wraps, and the sweet-savory combination of roast beef and mango makes them particularly satisfying.

- **¼ cup chili-garlic sauce**
- **1 tablespoon lime juice**
- **½ teaspoon soy sauce**
- **16 large Bibb or green leaf lettuce leaves**
- **¾ pound sliced lean roast beef, trimmed and cut into ½-inch strips**
- **¼ teaspoon salt**
- **2 large carrots, shredded**
- **1 small English (seedless) cucumber, halved lengthwise and sliced**
- **1 mango, peeled, pitted, and sliced**
- **3 scallions, sliced**
- **¾ cup lightly packed fresh cilantro leaves**
- **Lime wedges**

**1** To make sauce, stir together chili-garlic sauce, lime juice, and soy sauce in small bowl.

**2** Lay lettuce leaves on work surface. Divide beef evenly among lettuce leaves and sprinkle with salt. Top evenly with carrots, cucumber, mango, scallions, and cilantro; roll up to enclose filling. Serve with sauce and lime wedges.

**Per serving** (4 wraps and about 1 tablespoon sauce): 222 Cal, 5 g Total Fat, 2 g Sat Fat, 921 mg Sod, 23 g Total Carb, 15 g Sugar, 4 g Fib, 23 g Prot.

## Shopping tip

Made from a mix of chilies, garlic, salt, and vinegar, chili-garlic sauce can be found in supermarkets in the Asian-food aisle and in specialty-food stores. Add a small amount to marinades, sauces, and dips for some spiciness.

# Brown rice and veggie collard wraps

**Prep 25 min  Cook 2 min  Serves 4**

Broad collard green leaves replace tortillas or flatbread for a healthy, colorful sandwich wrap with 0 SmartPoints®. This firm-leafed veggie is packed with vitamin C, fiber, calcium, and iron and has a mild flavor that is family-friendly.

- **1 (8½-ounce) pouch microwavable precooked brown basmati rice**

DIPPING SAUCE

- **3 tablespoons soy sauce**
- **2 tablespoons water**
- **1 teaspoon Asian (dark) sesame oil**
- **1 teaspoon grated peeled fresh ginger**

WRAPS

- **8 collard green leaves (about 9 x 9 inches)**
- **1 cup matchstick-cut cucumber**
- **½ cup matchstick-cut carrot**
- **½ cup matchstick-cut red bell pepper**
- **½ cup coarsely chopped fresh cilantro**
- **1 scallion, thinly sliced**
- **1 Hass avocado, pitted, peeled, and cut into 16 slices**

**1** Heat rice in microwave according to package directions. Set aside to cool.

**2** Meanwhile, to make dipping sauce, stir together all ingredients in small serving bowl.

**3** To make wraps, cut off collard stems. Place leaves, veiny side up, on work surface. With small knife, shave off thick part of each rib so it is flat. (This will make collards easier to roll up.) Stack leaves and wrap in damp paper towels. Put on microwavable plate and microwave on High until leaves turn bright green and are flexible, about 1½ minutes.

**4** Mix together cucumber, carrot, bell pepper, cilantro, and scallion in medium bowl.

**5** Lay collard leaves on work surface, veiny side up. Put scant ¼ cup of rice on bottom half of each leaf. Top each leaf with 2 avocado slices and ⅓ cup of cucumber-carrot mixture. Fold in two opposite sides of each collard leaf, then roll up to enclose filling.

**6** Cut each wrap in half on diagonal. Serve with dipping sauce.

**Per serving** (2 wraps and 1½ tablespoons dipping sauce): 208 Cal, 8 g Total Fat, 1 g Sat Fat, 695 mg Sod, 30 g Total Carb, 3 g Sugar, 10 g Fib, 8 g Prot.

1/4 CUP
60 ml
WW

# Overstuffed microwave "baked" sweet potatoes

**Prep 10 min  Cook 8 min  Serves 4**

9 9 2

Give sweet potatoes just 8 minutes in a microwave and they come out soft, tender, and ready to eat. We've piled them high with a mix of zucchini, spinach, garlic, chipotles en adobo (for heat), and crumbly cotija cheese.

- **4 (½-pound) sweet potatoes, scrubbed**
- **2 teaspoons olive oil**
- **1 red bell pepper, cut into ½-inch dice**
- **1 zucchini, cut into ½-inch dice**
- **1 large garlic clove, crushed through a press**
- **1 teaspoon ground cumin**
- **½ teaspoon salt**
- **⅛ teaspoon black pepper**
- **1 (5-ounce) container baby spinach**
- **1 teaspoon minced chipotles en adobo**
- **4 tablespoons shredded cotija or crumbled feta**

**1** With fork, pierce each potato several times. Set on paper towel in microwave and microwave on High until just softened, about 8 minutes. Let potatoes cool about 5 minutes.

**2** Meanwhile, heat oil in large heavy nonstick skillet over medium-high heat. Add bell pepper and zucchini and cook, stirring occasionally, until crisp-tender, about 4 minutes. Add garlic, cumin, ¼ teaspoon salt, and black pepper and cook, stirring constantly, until fragrant, about 1 minute; stir in spinach. Reduce heat and cook, covered, 1 minute. Uncover and cook, stirring constantly, until spinach is wilted, about 1 minute longer.

**3** With small knife, slice off top third of potato. Scoop out potato flesh, leaving thin wall of potato. Put potato flesh into medium bowl; stir in chipotles en adobo and remaining ¼ teaspoon salt. Spoon potato mixture into potato skins, dividing evenly. Top each potato with ½ cup of vegetable mixture and 1 tablespoon cotija. Serve with tops on side.

**Per serving** (1 stuffed potato): 263 Cal, 5 g Total Fat, 1 g Sat Fat, 567 mg Sod, 50 g Total Carb, 12 g Sugar, 9 g Fib, 7 g Prot.

Chapter 3

# Dinner

START WITH THE BASE

## Basic roasted chicken breast

**Prep 5 min  Cook 30 min  Serves 4**

**4 (7-ounce) skin-on bone-in chicken breasts**
**1 teaspoon salt**
**½ teaspoon black pepper**

1 Preheat oven to 375°F. Spray large rimmed baking sheet with nonstick spray.

2 Sprinkle chicken with salt and pepper; place on prepared baking sheet. Bake until instant-read thermometer inserted in the center of chicken reaches 165°F, about 30 minutes. Separate chicken from bone; remove and discard skin.

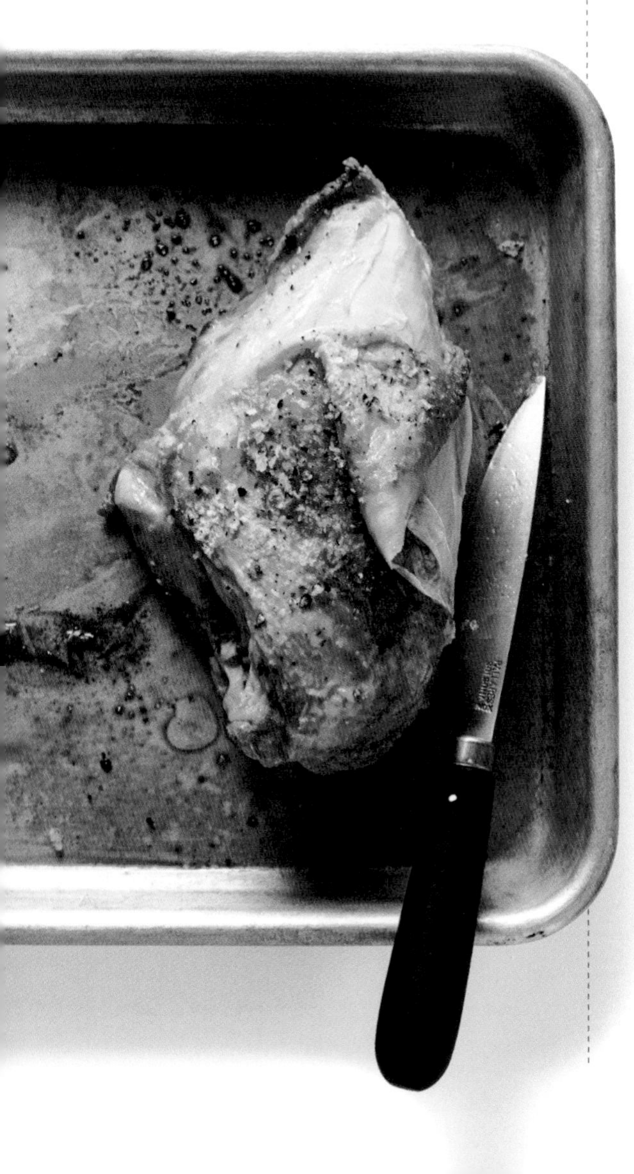

SOME DINNERS WE LOVE

## Hawaiian sheet pan chicken

**Prep 10 min  Cook 30 min  Serves 4**

Prepare chicken for **Basic roasted chicken breast,** placing chicken on one side of baking sheet. Combine **1½ cups fresh pineapple chunks, 1 large red bell pepper** cut into 1-inch chunks, and **1 medium red onion** cut into thin wedges on other side and toss with **⅓ cup reduced-sodium teriyaki sauce** and sprinkle with **black pepper.** Roast until chicken is cooked through and vegetables are tender and browned, about 30 minutes. Sprinkle with chopped **fresh cilantro.** Per serving: 1 chicken breast (skin discarded) and ½ cup pineapple and vegetables.

## Moroccan sheet pan chicken

**Prep 12 min  Cook 50 min  Serves 4**

Prepare chicken for **Basic roasted chicken breast,** placing chicken on one side of baking sheet. Combine **¾ pound quartered baby potatoes, 1 cup baby cut carrots** halved lengthwise, and **1 cup rinsed and drained canned chickpeas** on other side. Mix **1½ teaspoons ground cumin** and **1 teaspoon each paprika** and **turmeric** in custard cup; sprinkle over chicken and vegetables. Sprinkle vegetables with **½ teaspoon salt** and spray with **nonstick spray.** Top with **1 thinly sliced lemon.** Roast until chicken is cooked through, about 30 minutes; transfer to platter and cover to keep warm. Continue roasting vegetables until tender, about 20 minutes longer. Sprinkle with **⅓ cup chopped black olives.** Per serving: 1 chicken breast (skin discarded), about ½ cup vegetables, and generous 1 tablespoon olives.

## Italian sheet pan chicken

**Prep 15 minutes  Cook 30 min  Serves 4**

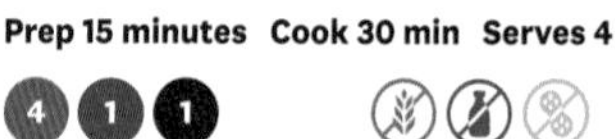

Prepare chicken for **Basic roasted chicken breast,** placing chicken on one side of prepared baking sheet. Sprinkle chicken with **½ teaspoon dried Italian seasoning.** Place **1 bunch broccolini (8 ounces), 1 cup grape tomatoes,** and **6 ounces halved cremini mushrooms** on other side of baking sheet. Place **4 (½-inch-thick) slices plain polenta from tube** alongside. Spray vegetables and polenta with nonstick spray; sprinkle vegetables and polenta with **½ teaspoon Italian seasoning, ½ teaspoon salt,** and **¼ teaspoon black pepper.** Roast until chicken is cooked through and vegetables are tender, about 30 minutes. Per serving: 1 chicken breast (skin discarded), about ¾ cup vegetables, and 1 slice polenta.

## Hawaiian sheet pan chicken

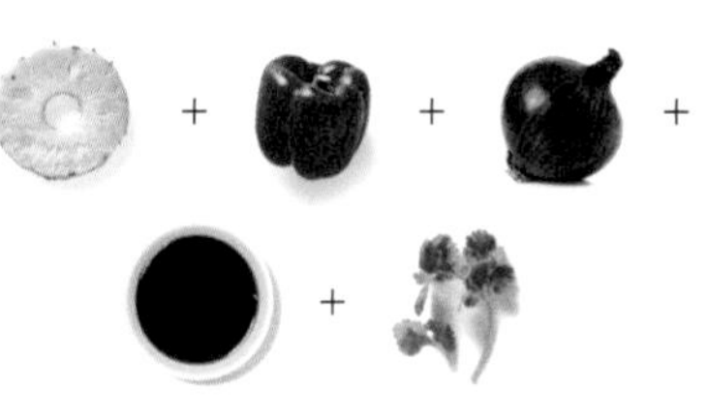

## Moroccan sheet pan chicken

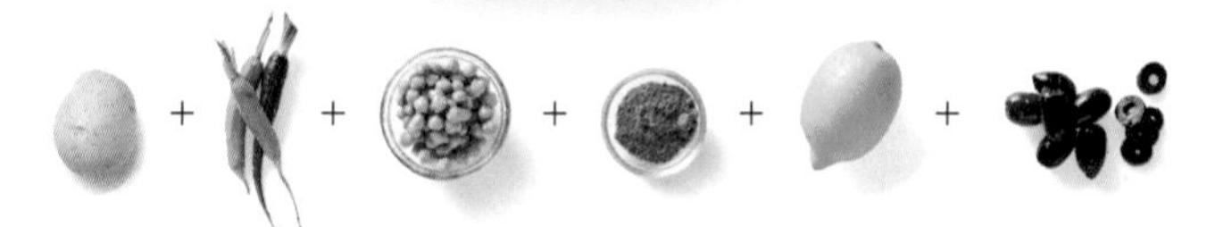

## Italian sheet pan chicken

START WITH THE BASE

## 2-ingredient pizza crust

**Prep 10 min Cook 20 min Serves 2**

Preheat oven to 400°F. Stir together **½ cup plain fat-free Greek yogurt** and **⅔ cup self-rising flour** in bowl. With floured hands, knead dough until smooth, about 2 minutes, adding more flour, 1 tablespoon at a time, if dough is sticky. Sprinkle sheet of parchment with flour. Place dough on parchment; cut dough in half. Use floured rolling pin to roll each piece of dough into 6–7 inch round. Transfer dough and parchment to baking sheet. Bake until bottom is golden, about 15 minutes. Top each pizza as desired (opposite) and bake until toppings are hot, 5–10 minutes.

BUILD YOUR OWN PIE

| BASE → | GREAT PROTEINS → | VEGGIE TOPPERS → | FLAVOR BOOSTERS → | FINISHING (SPRINKLE ON AFTER BAKING) |
|---|---|---|---|---|
| BBQ sauce | Cooked cubed chicken | Sliced drained artichokes in brine | Anchovies |   Baby arugula |
| Marinara sauce | Chopped clams | Thinly sliced bell pepper | Cooked crumbled bacon |  Fresh basil |
| Pesto | Goat cheese | Sautéed kale | Sliced olives |  Snipped chives |
| Part-skim ricotta | Shredded low-fat mozzarella | Sautéed mushrooms | Shredded Parmesan |  Truffle oil or olive oil |
| Puréed white beans | Turkey pepperoni | Thinly sliced sun-dried tomatoes | Red pepper flakes |  Fresh oregano |

# Some toppings we love

### Classic clam

2 1 1

3 tablespoons marinara sauce + ¼ cup chopped clams + large pinch red pepper flakes + 1 teaspoon fresh oregano leaves

### Pepperoni and basil

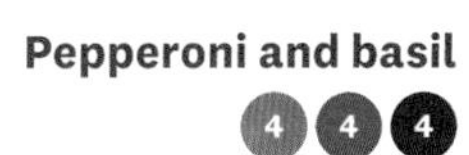


3 tablespoons marinara sauce + ¼ cup shredded low-fat mozzarella + 7 slices turkey pepperoni + 3 sliced basil leaves

### White artichoke

3 tablespoons part-skim ricotta + ¼ cup shredded low-fat mozzarella + ⅓ cup sliced drained artichokes in brine + large pinch red pepper flakes + ½ teaspoon truffle oil or olive oil

# Peruvian roast chicken with avocado salad

**Prep 15 min Cook 1 hr 10 min Serves 6**

3 3 3

If you don't have a roasting rack, you can place your chicken on a bed of veggies instead. Either way, lifting the chicken off the pan surface will help it cook evenly. Try 4 whole celery ribs or a few large carrots, halved lengthwise, in the roasting pan and set the chicken on top.

**2 tablespoons white-wine vinegar**
**1 tablespoon paprika**
**1 tablespoon ground cumin**
**5 garlic cloves, minced**
**1 teaspoon canola oil**
**1¾ teaspoons salt**
**⅛ teaspoon cayenne**
**1 (3½-pound) whole chicken, skin and wings removed and discarded and giblets removed**
**1 romaine lettuce heart, thinly sliced (about 6 cups)**
**½ small red onion, thinly sliced**
**½ small Hass avocado, pitted, peeled, and thinly sliced**
**Juice of ½ lime**
**Lime wedges, for serving**

**1** Preheat oven to 400°F. Spray roasting rack with nonstick spray and place in roasting pan.

**2** Stir together vinegar, paprika, cumin, garlic, oil, 1½ teaspoons salt, and cayenne in small bowl. Rub spice mixture all over meat and in cavity of chicken. Tie legs together with kitchen string. Place chicken, breast side up, on prepared rack in pan. Roast until instant-read thermometer inserted into thickest part of thigh (not touching bone) registers 165°F, about 1 hour. Transfer chicken to cutting board and let stand 10 minutes.

**3** Meanwhile, combine romaine and onion on serving platter or in salad bowl. Top with avocado; sprinkle with lime juice and remaining ¼ teaspoon salt.

**4** Carve chicken into 6 pieces and arrange on platter; serve with salad and lime wedges.

**Per serving** (1 piece chicken and 1 cup salad): 215 Cal, 7 g Total Fat, 1 g Sat Fat, 792 mg Sod, 8 g Carb, 2 g Sugar, 4 g Fib, 30 g Prot.

## Smart pointers

Want a bigger salad? Add halved cherry tomatoes and sliced cucumbers for 0 SmartPoints®.

# Chicken with silky eggplant in black bean sauce

**Prep 15 min Cook 20 min Serves 4**

5 2 2

An Instant Pot® gives this Chinese chicken and vegetable stew deep, slow-simmered taste in minutes. Its savory umami flavor comes from fermented black beans, a type of soy bean you'll find in Asian food stores or in the global-foods aisle of large supermarkets.

- **2 teaspoons canola oil**
- **1½ pounds skinless boneless chicken breast, cut into 1-inch chunks**
- **¼ teaspoon salt**
- **2 Chinese eggplants (about 1 pound), quartered lengthwise and cut into 2½-inch pieces**
- **4 garlic cloves, thinly sliced**
- **2 teaspoons minced peeled fresh ginger**
- **¼ teaspoon red pepper flakes**
- **¾ cup chicken broth**
- **2½ tablespoons fermented black beans**
- **2 tablespoons low-sodium soy sauce**
- **1 tablespoon rice wine vinegar**
- **1 tablespoon cornstarch**
- **1 teaspoon sugar**
- **1 small red bell pepper, cut into 1-inch pieces**
- **5 scallions, cut into 1-inch lengths**
- **1 tablespoon sesame seeds**

**1** Add oil to 6-quart Instant Pot; press Sauté and set cooking time for 15 minutes. When Hot is displayed, add half of chicken; sprinkle with ⅛ teaspoon salt. Cook, stirring occasionally, until browned and cooked through, about 3 minutes. With slotted spoon, transfer to large bowl. Repeat with remaining chicken and ⅛ teaspoon salt. Cover chicken to keep warm.

**2** Add eggplant to pot and cook, stirring occasionally, until browned, about 3 minutes. Add garlic, ginger, and pepper flakes; cook, stirring constantly, until fragrant, about 1 minute. Add broth and black beans. Press Cancel to turn off pot. Lock lid, making sure vent is closed.

**3** Press Pressure Cook and select High Pressure; set cooking time for 5 minutes. When time is up, press Cancel to turn off pot. Move steam-release valve to Venting position to quickly release pressure. Remove lid.

**4** Meanwhile, stir together soy sauce, vinegar, cornstarch, and sugar; set aside.

**5** Using slotted spoon, transfer eggplant to chicken in bowl; cover to keep warm.

**6** Press Sauté and set cooking time for 15 minutes. Add cornstarch mixture to pot and cook, stirring constantly, until mixture bubbles and thickens, about 2 minutes. Add bell pepper and scallions and cook 1 minute longer. Pour sauce over chicken and eggplant and sprinkle with sesame seeds.

**Per serving** (1½ cups): 350 Cal, 9 g Total Fat, 2 g Sat Fat, 1,074 mg Sod, 22 g Total Carb, 11 g Sugar, 9 g Fib, 45 g Prot.

## Serving idea

Quick-cooking rice noodles are perfect for soaking up the sauce of this dish; plan on a cup of cooked noodles per person.

# Jerk chicken with quinoa, mint, and mango

**Prep 15 min  Cook 23 min  Serves 4**

8 6 2

A salad with quinoa and sweet mango makes a fantastic accompaniment to spicy Jamaican-flavored chicken cutlets. We suggest dry jerk seasoning, but jerk paste works, too: Rub about 1 tablespoon into the cutlets; protect your skin from the fiery paste by wearing kitchen gloves.

- **1 cup tricolor quinoa, rinsed and drained**
- **1½ cups water**
- **¾ teaspoon salt**
- **2 teaspoons grated lime zest**
- **¼ cup lime juice**
- **4 teaspoons olive oil**
- **¼ teaspoon black pepper**
- **2 tablespoons minced red onion**
- **4 (¼-pound) chicken breast cutlets**
- **1 tablespoon jerk seasoning**
- **1 large mango, peeled, pitted, and thinly sliced**
- **1 red bell pepper, thinly sliced**
- **½ cup chopped fresh mint**
- **⅓ cup chopped fresh cilantro**
- **2 scallions, thinly sliced**
- **4 lime wedges**

**1** Set small saucepan over medium heat. Add quinoa and cook, stirring frequently, until dry and fragrant, about 5 minutes. Stir in water and ¼ teaspoon salt; bring to boil over high heat. Reduce heat to low and simmer, covered, until liquid is absorbed and quinoa is tender, about 15 minutes. Remove from heat and let stand 5 minutes. Fluff quinoa with fork. Transfer to large bowl and let cool slightly.

**2** Meanwhile, to make dressing, whisk together lime zest and juice, oil, ¼ teaspoon salt, and pepper in small bowl. Stir in onion.

**3** Sprinkle both sides of chicken cutlets with jerk seasoning and remaining ¼ teaspoon salt. Spray ridged grill pan with nonstick spray and set over medium-high heat. Place chicken on grill pan and grill until cooked through, about 3 minutes per side.

**4** Add mango, bell pepper, mint, cilantro, and scallions to quinoa in bowl; pour dressing over and toss to coat. Divide chicken and quinoa evenly among 4 plates. Serve with lime wedges.

**Per serving** (1 chicken cutlet and 1½ cups quinoa salad): 417 Cal, 11 g Total Fat, 2 g Sat Fat, 647 mg Sod, 48 g Total Carb, 16 g Sugar, 7 g Fib, 33 g Prot.

## Prep ahead

Make a big batch of quinoa on the weekend to use in recipes like this one, or to serve as a side dish all week long. Cooked quinoa will keep refrigerated for up to 4 days.

# Sage and blue cheese chicken burgers

**Prep 15 min Cook 10 min Serves 4**

8 6 6

What makes these lean chicken burgers so moist and rich-tasting? The combo of shredded apple, onion, and sage. A creamy drizzle of blue cheese dressing puts them over the top. If you'd like, double up when you make the burger patties and freeze extras for later.

**1 pound ground skinless chicken breast**
**⅓ cup shredded sweet apple, such as Gala or Fuji**
**3 tablespoons finely chopped red onion**
**3 tablespoons whole-wheat panko (Japanese) bread crumbs**
**1 tablespoon finely chopped fresh sage**
**1 tablespoon hot pepper sauce**
**1 tablespoon Worcestershire sauce**
**¼ teaspoon + 1 pinch salt**
**¼ cup crumbled Gorgonzola or other blue cheese**
**2 tablespoons low-fat buttermilk**
**2 teaspoons mayonnaise**
**⅛ teaspoon black pepper**
**4 whole-wheat sandwich thins, split and toasted**
**1 small tomato, sliced**
**4 small Boston or Bibb lettuce leaves**

**1** Combine chicken, apple, onion, panko, sage, pepper sauce, Worcestershire, and ¼ teaspoon salt in large bowl. With damp hands, form mixture into 4 (½-inch-thick) patties. Lightly spray patties on both sides with nonstick spray.

**2** Set nonstick ridged grill pan over medium heat. Place patties on pan and cook until browned and instant-read thermometer inserted into side of burger registers 165°F, 4–5 minutes per side.

**3** Meanwhile, to make dressing, stir together Gorgonzola, buttermilk, mayonnaise, pepper, and remaining pinch salt in small bowl. Serve burgers in sandwich thins topped with dressing, tomato, and lettuce.

**Per serving** (1 burger and 1 tablespoon dressing): 323 Cal, 9 g Total Fat, 3 g Sat Fat, 729 mg Sod, 29 g Total Carb, 6 g Sugar, 6 g Fib, 33 g Prot.

## Serving idea

Baked sweet potato fries are a quick and easy side for these burgers. Put 1½ ounces of fries in the oven for each serving you want. Start baking them just before you begin prepping the burgers and both will be done at about the same time.

# Chicken thighs with apples, onions, and sauerkraut

**Prep 15 min  Cook 20 min  Serves 4**

4 4 4

Sweet apple mellows the tang of sauerkraut in this comforting Instant Pot® chicken dinner. Fresh dill added at the end lends wonderful bright flavor to the rustic dish.

- **4 (6-ounce) skinless bone-in chicken thighs**
- **¾ teaspoon kosher salt**
- **¼ teaspoon black pepper**
- **1 medium onion, sliced**
- **1 Golden Delicious apple, cored and cut into chunks**
- **2 cups drained refrigerated (bagged or jarred) sauerkraut**
- **½ teaspoon caraway seeds, or to taste**
- **¼ cup chopped fresh dill, + additional for garnish**
- **¼ cup sliced scallions**
- **Whole-grain mustard, for serving (optional)**

**1** Spray chicken with olive oil nonstick spray and sprinkle with ½ teaspoon salt and pepper. Press Sauté on 6-quart Instant Pot and set cooking time for 15 minutes. When Hot is displayed, add chicken and cook until browned, about 4 minutes. Turn and cook until browned on second side, about 2 minutes longer. Transfer to plate.

**2** Add onion and apple to pot and cook, stirring occasionally, until onion is almost softened, about 2 minutes. Stir in sauerkraut, caraway seeds, and remaining ¼ teaspoon salt. Place chicken on top of sauerkraut mixture. Press Cancel to turn off pot. Lock lid, making sure vent is closed.

**3** Press Pressure Cook and select Low Pressure; set cooking time for 7 minutes. When time is up, press Cancel to turn off pot. Allow pressure to naturally release for 5 minutes. Move steam-release valve to Venting position to release remaining pressure. Remove lid.

**4** Arrange chicken on serving platter. Stir ¼ cup dill into sauerkraut mixture; spoon sauerkraut onto platter surrounding chicken. Sprinkle with scallions and additional dill. Serve with mustard, if desired.

**Per serving** (1 chicken thigh and ¾ cup sauerkraut): 257 Cal, 7 g Total Fat, 2 g Sat Fat, 994 mg Sod, 12 g Total Carb, 7 g Sugar, 4 g Fib, 34 g Prot.

## Shopping tip

For fresher flavor and the most probiotic benefits, look for sauerkraut that contains only cabbage, water, and salt and is sold refrigerated. The addition of preservatives can give it a harsh taste, and pasteurization can kill gut-friendly probiotics.

# Korean chicken drumsticks

**Prep 15 min  Cook 45 min  Serves 4**

Drumsticks are often overlooked, but they're an inexpensive yet flavor-rich cut of chicken for weeknight meals. Be sure to use foil to line the baking sheet for easiest cleanup.

- **8 (4½-ounce) skinless chicken drumsticks**
- **2 tablespoons soy sauce**
- **1 tablespoon rice wine vinegar**
- **1 teaspoon Asian (dark) sesame oil**
- **3 garlic cloves, minced**
- **2 teaspoons grated peeled fresh ginger**
- **2 teaspoons light brown sugar**
- **1 teaspoon sriracha**
- **4 heads baby bok choy, halved lengthwise**
- **2 teaspoons black or white sesame seeds, or a combination**

**1** Preheat oven to 375°F. Line small rimmed baking sheet with foil.

**2** Using sharp knife, cut shallow slits in drumsticks (do not cut to bone). Place chicken on prepared baking sheet. Combine soy sauce, vinegar, oil, garlic, ginger, brown sugar, and sriracha in small bowl. Pour half of sauce over drumsticks and turn to coat. Bake 15 minutes.

**3** Turn drumsticks and spoon remaining sauce over. Bake until chicken is tender and sauce is slightly sticky, about 20 minutes.

**4** Transfer chicken and juices to plate and cover with foil to keep warm. (If you'd like, reduce the pan juices to a glaze by simmering them over medium-low heat in a small saucepan until slightly thickened, about 4 minutes.)

**5** Meanwhile, bring 1 inch water to boil in bottom of steamer basket; place bok choy in basket and steam until bright green and just tender, 4–5 minutes. Place drumsticks on platter, drizzle with pan juices, and surround with bok choy. Sprinkle with sesame seeds.

**Per serving** (2 drumsticks and 1 baby bok choy): 307 Cal, 10 g Total Fat, 3 g Sat Fat, 746 mg Sod, 5 g Total Carb, 2 g Sugar, 1 g Fib, 50 g Prot.

## Serving idea

Half a cup of white rice per serving will soak up all the wonderful sauce in this chicken dish.

# Sweet potato lasagna with turkey and sage

**Prep 30 min Cook 1 hr 40 min Serves 8**

This comfort-food lasagna replaces the usual noodles with layers of sweet potatoes. Slice the potatoes thinly so they cook evenly. A mandoline is perfect for the job, but a sharp knife will work; if using a knife, you may find it easier to cut them into rounds (crosswise) rather than lengthwise.

- **2 teaspoons olive oil**
- **1 large onion, diced**
- **2 carrots, diced**
- **3 garlic cloves, finely chopped**
- **1 tablespoon + 1½ teaspoons chopped fresh sage**
- **1 pound ground skinless turkey breast**
- **1½ tablespoons tomato paste**
- **¼ cup red wine**
- **1 (14½-ounce) can diced tomatoes**
- **¾ teaspoon + pinch salt**
- **¼ teaspoon + ⅛ teaspoon black pepper**
- **½ cup part-skim ricotta**
- **1 large egg, beaten**
- **2 (¾-pound) sweet potatoes, peeled**
- **8 ounces spinach leaves**
- **½ cup shredded part-skim mozzarella**

**1** To make sauce, heat oil in large saucepan over medium-high heat. Add onion and carrots and cook, stirring frequently, until softened, 5–6 minutes. Stir in garlic and 1 tablespoon sage; cook, stirring frequently, until fragrant, about 1 minute. Stir in turkey, breaking it up with wooden spoon. Add tomato paste and cook, stirring often, until turkey is no longer pink, about 5 minutes. Add wine and simmer until almost evaporated, 1–2 minutes. Stir in tomatoes, 3 tablespoons water, ¾ teaspoon salt, and ¼ teaspoon pepper. Reduce heat and simmer, covered, until vegetables are very tender, about 15 minutes, adding more water if needed.

**2** Meanwhile, preheat oven to 400°F.

**3** Stir together ricotta, egg, 1½ teaspoons sage, remaining pinch salt, and remaining ⅛ teaspoon pepper in small bowl; set aside. Using mandoline, V-slicer, or very sharp knife, cut potatoes into very thin lengthwise slices (about 1/10-inch thick). Put spinach in large bowl and cover with boiling water. Let stand 1 minute; drain and let cool. Squeeze dry and roughly chop.

**4** Spread thin layer of sauce over bottom of 9-inch square (2-quart) baking dish. Cover with one third of potato slices, overlapping slightly. Spread half of remaining sauce over potatoes. Cover with another third of potato slices and top with spinach. Spoon ricotta mixture on top and spread evenly. Top with remaining potato slices, remaining sauce, and mozzarella. Cover loosely with sheet of nonstick foil.

**5** Place lasagna on baking sheet; bake until potatoes in center of lasagna are very tender when pierced with tip of paring knife, about 1 hour. Remove foil and bake until cheese is lightly browned, about 10 minutes. Let stand 10 minutes and cut into 8 portions.

**Per serving** (⅛ of lasagna): 229 Cal, 5 g Total Fat, 2 g Sat Fat, 616 mg Sod, 26 g Total Carb, 7 g Sugar, 5 g Fib, 20 g Prot.

## Serving idea

Lasagna calls for a light side dish. We like a tricolor salad of radicchio, endive, and arugula dressed with olive oil, red-wine vinegar, salt, and pepper. A 1-teaspoon serving of olive oil won't increase the SmartPoints® by much.

OPINEL

# Tex-Mex turkey cutlets with corn salad

**Prep 15 min  Cook 6 min  Serves 4**

Looking for an alternative to chicken breast? Try turkey cutlets: They're just as quick-cooking and versatile as their chicken counterparts. Here they make a quick dinner with a Southwest-inspired corn-and-tomato salad.

- **2 cups fresh corn kernels (about 4 ears)**
- **1 green bell pepper, diced**
- **1 tomato, diced**
- **2 scallions, thinly sliced**
- **1 jalapeño pepper, seeded and minced**
- **2 tablespoons chopped fresh cilantro**
- **2 tablespoons lime juice**
- **2 teaspoons extra-virgin olive oil**
- **¾ teaspoon salt**
- **4 (¼-pound) turkey breast cutlets**
- **¼ teaspoon black pepper**
- **⅛ teaspoon cayenne**
- **Lime wedges**

**1** To make salad, mix together corn, bell pepper, tomato, scallions, jalapeño, cilantro, lime juice, oil, and ¼ teaspoon salt in serving bowl.

**2** Spray ridged grill pan with nonstick spray. Set over medium-high heat.

**3** Sprinkle turkey with remaining ½ teaspoon salt, black pepper, and cayenne. Put turkey on grill pan and cook until golden and cooked through, about 3 minutes per side. Serve turkey with corn salad and lime wedges.

**Per serving** (1 turkey cutlet and 1 cup corn salad): 233 Cal, 5 g Total Fat, 1 g Sat Fat, 571 mg Sod, 20 g Total Carb, 4 g Sugar, 3 g Fib, 30 g Prot.

## Prep ahead

Make the corn salad up to 2 days ahead and refrigerate, stirring in the cilantro just before serving to keep it fresh and vibrant. While you're at it, make a double batch and enjoy the extras inside a sandwich wrap or on top of any kind of greens.

# Shepherd's pie with ground turkey

**Prep 25 min  Cook 1 hr 10 min  Serves 8**

The classic Irish casserole topped with mashed potatoes usually has a filling of ground lamb or beef. Here we substitute ground turkey to make it extra-lean and reduce the SmartPoints®.

- **2 large russet potatoes (about 1¾ pounds), peeled and cut into 2-inch chunks**
- **⅓ cup reduced-fat sour cream**
- **1 tablespoon unsalted butter**
- **1 teaspoon salt**
- **2 teaspoons olive oil**
- **3 carrots, diced**
- **2 celery stalks, diced**
- **1 small onion, diced**
- **1 cup fresh or frozen, thawed corn kernels**
- **2 garlic cloves, finely chopped**
- **1 pound ground skinless turkey breast**
- **1½ tablespoons tomato paste**
- **1 teaspoon dried rosemary**
- **1 teaspoon dried thyme**
- **½ teaspoon black pepper**
- **2 tablespoons all-purpose flour**
- **1¼ cups chicken or beef broth**

**1** Set rack in upper third of oven and preheat to 400°F. Spray 2-quart casserole dish or 7 x 11-inch baking dish with nonstick spray.

**2** Put potatoes in medium saucepan and cover with 1 inch cold water. Bring to boil over high heat; reduce heat and simmer until potatoes are fork-tender, about 15 minutes. Drain and return to saucepan. Add sour cream, butter, and ½ teaspoon salt and mash with potato masher or large fork until smooth.

**3** Meanwhile, heat oil in large skillet over medium heat. Add carrots, celery, and onion; cook, stirring frequently, until softened, about 5 minutes. Stir in corn and garlic and cook, stirring constantly, 1 minute. Transfer to bowl. Return skillet to heat and add turkey; cook, breaking up turkey with side of wooden spoon, until cooked through, about 5 minutes. Stir in tomato paste, rosemary, thyme, pepper, and remaining ½ teaspoon salt and cook 2 minutes longer. Stir in carrot mixture. Stir in flour and broth and simmer until thickened, about 2 minutes.

**4** Transfer turkey mixture to prepared casserole dish. Spread mashed potatoes over top, making sure to cover edges. Bake until potatoes are browned, 35–40 minutes. Cool at least 20 minutes before serving.

**Per serving** (⅛ of casserole): 214 Cal, 5 g Total Fat, 2 g Sat Fat, 599 mg Sod, 27 g Total Carb, 3 g Sugar, 3 g Fib, 16 g Prot.

## Prep ahead

You can assemble the casserole up to 2 days ahead, cover it, and refrigerate it unbaked. Remove the covering before popping it into the oven; add an extra few minutes to the cooking time.

STAUB
STAUB

# Filets mignons with fresh herb sauce

**Prep 20 min   Cook 5 min   Serves 4**

Here's tender filet mignon at its best and easiest: pan-seared and served with a bold parsley and cilantro sauce. If you like, make extra sauce to spoon over rice, broiled salmon, sliced tomatoes, or steamed green beans another day.

- **1 cup lightly packed fresh flat-leaf parsley leaves**
- **½ cup lightly packed fresh cilantro leaves**
- **2 garlic cloves, crushed with side of large knife**
- **¼ cup water**
- **1 tablespoon red-wine vinegar**
- **3 teaspoons olive oil**
- **1 teaspoon lemon juice**
- **1 teaspoon salt**
- **¼ teaspoon black pepper**
- **4 (¼-pound) lean filets mignons, about 1-inch thick, trimmed**

**1** To make herb sauce, combine parsley, cilantro, garlic, water, vinegar, 2 teaspoons oil, lemon juice, ½ teaspoon salt, and pepper in blender or food processor and pulse until smooth. Set aside.

**2** Coat large heavy nonstick skillet with remaining 1 teaspoon oil and set over medium-high heat. Sprinkle beef with remaining ½ teaspoon salt. Place beef in skillet and cook until instant-read thermometer inserted into side of steak registers 145°F, 2–3 minutes per side. Serve with herb sauce.

**Per serving** (1 filet mignon and ⅓ cup sauce): 208 Cal, 10 g Total Fat, 3 g Sat Fat, 655 mg Sod, 2 g Total Carb, 0 g Sugar, 1 g Fib, 26 g Prot.

## Serving idea

Steamed baby carrots make a colorful side dish; see our recipe on page xxxi for an easy, tasty version.

# Steak au poivre

**Prep 15 min   Cook 13 min   Serves 4**

This one-skillet dinner features sliced zucchini cooked with shallots in a mustardy brandy sauce to serve with peppercorn-crusted filets mignons. It's quick enough for weeknights, but also impressive enough for entertaining.

- **1 tablespoon whole black peppercorns, crushed**
- **4 (5-ounce) lean filets mignons, trimmed**
- **¾ teaspoon salt**
- **2 teaspoons olive oil**
- **3 small zucchini, halved lengthwise and thinly sliced**
- **3 shallots, finely chopped**
- **3 tablespoons brandy, bourbon, or beef broth**
- **½ cup beef broth**
- **1 tablespoon Dijon mustard**

**1** Spread peppercorns on plate. Coat steaks on one side with peppercorns, pressing so they adhere. Sprinkle with ½ teaspoon salt.

**2** Heat oil in large heavy nonstick skillet over medium-high heat. Add steaks, peppercorn side down, and cook until instant-read thermometer inserted into side of steak registers 145°F, about 3 minutes per side. Transfer to plate and loosely cover with foil.

**3** Add zucchini, shallots, and remaining ¼ teaspoon salt to skillet and cook, stirring, until zucchini is crisp-tender, about 3 minutes. Add brandy and cook 20 seconds (if brandy flames, cover skillet with lid and remove from heat until it dies down).

**4** Whisk broth and mustard into skillet until smooth. Simmer until sauce is slightly thickened, about 3 minutes. Serve with steaks.

**Per serving** (1 steak with ⅔ cup vegetables and sauce): 289 Cal, 11 g Total Fat, 4 g Sat Fat, 721 mg Sod, 6 g Total Carb, 3 g Sugar, 2 g Fib, 33 g Prot.

# Korean rice and short rib bowls

**Prep 15 min  Cook 25 min  Serves 4**

12 12 9

An Instant Pot® makes succulent beef short ribs possible in a fraction of the time. The pear, soy sauce, ginger, and sriracha turn into a sweet, salty, spicy sauce, exceptionally good drizzled over the ribs and rice.

- **3 scallions, sliced, white and green parts separated**
- **¼ cup shredded ripe pear**
- **3 tablespoons reduced-sodium soy sauce**
- **2 teaspoons rice wine vinegar**
- **2 teaspoons minced peeled fresh ginger**
- **1 teaspoon Asian (dark) sesame oil**
- **½ teaspoon sriracha, plus additional for serving**
- **4 (3½-ounce) trimmed flanken-style beef short ribs or boneless short ribs, each cut between bones into 4 pieces**
- **2 cups cooked brown rice, warmed**
- **1 cup kimchi**
- **1 cup matchstick-cut cucumber**
- **1 cup matchstick-cut carrot**
- **½ red bell pepper, cut into matchstick strips**
- **½ cup lightly packed fresh cilantro leaves**
- **2 teaspoons toasted sesame seeds**
- **Lime wedges**

**1** Stir together white part of scallions, pear, soy sauce, vinegar, ginger, oil, and ½ teaspoon sriracha in medium bowl. Add short ribs and toss until coated evenly. Let stand at room temperature about 15 minutes, tossing occasionally.

**2** Spray bottom of 6-quart Instant Pot with cooking spray. Add short rib mixture to pot. Lock lid, making sure vent is closed. Press Pressure Cook and select High Pressure; set cooking time for 20 minutes. When time is up, press Cancel to turn off pot. Allow pressure to release naturally for 15 minutes. Move steam-release valve to Venting position to release any remaining pressure. Remove lid.

**3** Transfer ribs to bowl. Pour cooking juices into glass measure; skim off and discard fat.

**4** Divide rice evenly among 4 bowls; drizzle each with 2 tablespoons cooking juices. Top evenly with ribs, kimchi, cucumber, carrots, and bell pepper. Sprinkle with scallion greens, cilantro, and sesame seeds. Serve with sriracha and lime wedges.

**Per serving** (1 bowl): 482 Cal, 21 g Total Fat, 8 g Sat Fat, 724 mg Sod, 36 g Total Carb, 5 g Sugar, 4 g Fib, 36 g Prot.

## Shopping tip

Sometimes called cross-cut ribs, flanken-style ribs are cut so that each piece has three or four cross-cut ribs surrounded by meat. Look for them at larger supermarkets and most butcher shops.

# Lemon-basil pork and vegetable kebabs

**Prep 20 min Cook 12 min Serves 4**

Colorful garden veggies and cubes of lean pork make for terrific kebabs. As an alternative, you can make this dish by grilling the pork chops whole and placing the vegetables in a grill basket to cook.

**Grated zest and juice from 1 large lemon**
**4 teaspoons canola oil**
**3 garlic cloves, minced**
**½ teaspoon salt**
**¼ teaspoon black pepper**
**1 pound lean boneless pork chops, trimmed and cut into ¾-inch cubes**
**1 zucchini, halved lengthwise and cut into ½-inch slices**
**1 yellow squash, halved lengthwise and cut into ½-inch slices**
**1 pint cherry tomatoes**
**1 red onion, cut into 8 wedges**
**¼ cup small basil leaves**
**Lemon wedges**

**1** Spray grill rack with nonstick spray; preheat grill to medium high or prepare medium-hot fire.

**2** Stir together lemon zest and juice, oil, garlic, salt, and pepper in large bowl; add pork, zucchini, yellow squash, tomatoes, and onion; toss to coat. Thread onto 16 (6-inch) metal skewers. (If using wooden skewers, soak in water 30 minutes to prevent them from charring.)

**3** Place skewers on grill rack and grill, turning frequently, until browned and cooked through, 10–12 minutes. Transfer to serving platter and sprinkle with basil. Serve with lemon wedges.

**Per serving** (4 kebabs): 261 Cal, 12 g Total Fat, 3 g Sat Fat, 361 mg Sod, 14 g Total Carb, 7 g Sugar, 4 g Fib, 27 g Prot.

## Serving idea

Accompany these colorful kebabs with a half-cup side of cooked couscous per serving.

# Lemony pork piccata

**Prep 20 min   Cook 8 min   Serves 4**

6 6 6

Quickly sautéed pork chops in a lemony sauce flavored with capers and parsley reward less than 30 minutes of prep and cooking with an elegant main dish. Just a small amount of grated Parmesan in the gremolata-like topping goes a long way.

**4 (¼-pound) lean boneless pork loin chops, trimmed**
**2 tablespoons all-purpose flour**
**1¼ teaspoons kosher salt**
**¼ teaspoon black pepper**
**3 teaspoons unsalted butter**
**2 teaspoons olive oil**
**2 large shallots, finely chopped**
**1 small garlic clove, minced**
**½ cup chicken broth**
**Juice of 1 lemon**
**1 tablespoon nonpareil (tiny) capers, drained**
**2 tablespoons chopped fresh flat-leaf parsley**
**1 tablespoon grated Parmesan**
**1 teaspoon grated lemon zest**

1 Place pork between two pieces of plastic wrap. With meat mallet or rolling pin, pound to ⅛-inch thickness.

2 Mix together flour, 1 teaspoon salt, and pepper in large shallow bowl. Coat pork with seasoned flour, shaking off excess.

3 Melt 2 teaspoons butter with oil in large heavy nonstick skillet over high heat. Add pork and cook until browned, about 2 minutes per side. Transfer to plate. Cover to keep warm.

4 Add shallots, garlic, broth, lemon juice, and capers to skillet, scraping up any browned bits from bottom of pan; bring to boil. Reduce heat to medium and cook, stirring once or twice, until sauce is slightly reduced, about 2 minutes. Stir in remaining 1 teaspoon butter and ¼ teaspoon salt. Return pork with any accumulated juices to skillet, turning pork to coat with sauce.

5 Place 1 cutlet on each of 4 plates and spoon sauce over. Mix together parsley, Parmesan, and lemon zest in cup and sprinkle over pork.

**Per serving** (1 pork cutlet and about 2 tablespoons sauce): 253 Cal, 12 g Total Fat, 5 g Sat Fat, 851 mg Sod, 9 g Total Carb, 2 g Sugar, 1 g Fib, 26 g Prot.

## Smart pointers

**Serve the piccata with ZeroPoint™ steamed zucchini noodles or other veggie noodles. You can make your own with a spiralizer, or buy them in the produce section of most supermarkets.**

# Lamb korma with banana raita

**Prep 20 min  Cook 26 min  Serves 4**

4 4 4

Turn to your Instant Pot® to make leg of lamb melt-in-your-mouth tender without hours of simmering. The rich, aromatic combination of coconut milk, tomato, and spices makes korma a Southern Indian favorite.

**KORMA**

- **1 large red onion, coarsely chopped**
- **1 (½-inch) piece peeled fresh ginger, finely chopped**
- **3 garlic cloves, finely chopped**
- **2 tablespoons coarsely chopped cilantro stems**
- **2 teaspoons curry powder**
- **¾ teaspoon ground cumin**
- **½ teaspoon cinnamon**
- **¾ teaspoon salt, or to taste**
- **1 (14½-ounce) can diced tomatoes**
- **½ cup light (low-fat) coconut milk**
- **1 pound lean lamb leg, trimmed and cut into ¾-inch pieces**
- **2 cups (¾-inch) cubes butternut squash**
- **3 tablespoons chopped fresh cilantro**

**RAITA**

- **½ small banana, diced**
- **½ cup plain low-fat yogurt**
- **2 tablespoons chopped fresh cilantro**
- **½ teaspoon grated peeled fresh ginger**
- **¼ teaspoon ground cumin**

## Serving idea

Riced cauliflower is a great ZeroPoint™ accompaniment to this saucy korma. Or try brown rice for nutty flavor and a dose of whole grains.

**1** Spray bottom of 6-quart Instant Pot with nonstick spray; press Sauté. When Hot is displayed, add onion, ginger, garlic, and cilantro stems. Cook, stirring occasionally, until softened, about 3 minutes. Add curry powder, cumin, cinnamon, and salt and cook, stirring constantly, until fragrant, about 30 seconds. Add tomatoes and coconut milk and stir to scrape up browned bits from bottom of pan. Stir in lamb. Press Cancel to turn off pot. Lock lid, making sure vent is closed.

**2** Press Pressure Cook and select High Pressure; set cooking time for 14 minutes. When time is up, press Cancel to turn off pot. Move steam-release valve to Venting position to quickly release pressure. Remove lid. Stir in squash. Lock lid, making sure vent is closed.

**3** Press Pressure Cook and select High Pressure; set cooking time for 3 minutes. When time is up, press Cancel to turn off pot. Move steam-release valve to Venting position to release pressure. Remove lid. Stir in cilantro.

**4** Meanwhile, to make raita, stir together all ingredients in serving bowl. Serve with lamb.

**Per serving** (1¾ cups korma and 3 tablespoons raita): 262 Cal, 7 g Total Fat, 3 g Sat Fat, 703 mg Sod, 25 g Total Carb, 10 g Sugar, 4 g Fib, 28 g Prot.

# Grilled sea bass with tomato vinaigrette

**Prep 15 min Cook 10 min Serves 4**

3 2 2

Here's one of the quickest, most delicious fish dishes we know. The sea bass is grilled along with Meyer lemons, a cross between a regular lemon and a mandarin orange. They have a distinctive floral flavor and are less acidic than regular lemons.

- **8 ounces (about 1½ cups) cherry tomatoes, diced**
- **2 tablespoons finely chopped shallot**
- **1 teaspoon drained capers, roughly chopped**
- **1 small garlic clove, finely chopped**
- **1 tablespoon lemon juice**
- **4 teaspoons extra-virgin olive oil**
- **¼ teaspoon + ⅛ teaspoon salt**
- **¼ teaspoon black pepper**
- **2 Meyer lemons or regular lemons, halved**
- **4 (4-ounce) skin-on sea bass fillets**
- **1 bunch (about ¾ pound) asparagus, trimmed**
- **1 tablespoon chopped fresh chives**
- **2 teaspoons finely chopped fresh parsley**

1 To make vinaigrette, combine tomatoes, shallot, capers, garlic, lemon juice, 2 teaspoons oil, ¼ teaspoon salt, and ⅛ teaspoon pepper in small saucepan. Set aside.

2 Spray large ridged grill pan with nonstick spray and set over medium-high heat.

3 Brush cut sides of lemons and sea bass with remaining 2 teaspoons oil. Sprinkle fish with remaining ⅛ teaspoon salt and ⅛ teaspoon pepper. Place fish, flesh side down, and lemons, cut side down, in pan. Cook until fish is just opaque in center, 2–3 minutes per side, and lemons are browned on cut side only (do not turn lemons), about 3-4 minutes.

4 Meanwhile, bring medium skillet half filled with water to boil. Add asparagus and cook until crisp-tender, about 3 minutes; drain.

5 Set vinaigrette over medium heat and cook, stirring occasionally, until warmed, about 3 minutes. Remove from heat and stir in chives and parsley.

6 Divide fish, asparagus, and lemons evenly among 4 plates. Spoon vinaigrette evenly over fish and asparagus.

**Per serving** (about 5 asparagus spears, 1 sea bass fillet, 2½ tablespoons dressing, and ½ lemon): 195 Cal, 7 g Total Fat, 1 g Sat Fat, 318 mg Sod, 11 g Total Carb, 5 g Sugar, 4 g Fib, 24 g Prot.

## Shopping tip

Look for Meyer lemons in larger supermarkets and specialty-food stores from about November through February; substitute regular lemons in this recipe if they're not in season.

# Salmon with melted leeks and miso butter

**Prep 15 min  Cook 10 min  Serves 4**

10 3 3

The salmon in this speedy Instant Pot® dish stays supermoist when cooked with the pot's steam function. Miso butter lends a nice touch of umami to the dish, along with a healthy dose of probiotics.

- **3 large leeks (white and light green parts only), halved, sliced, and rinsed (about 3 cups)**
- **½ cup water**
- **2 teaspoons + 1 tablespoon unsalted butter, softened**
- **¼ teaspoon salt**
- **4 (5-ounce) skin-on salmon fillets**
- **2 teaspoons grated peeled fresh ginger**
- **1½ teaspoons reduced-sodium soy sauce**
- **1½ tablespoons white miso**
- **1 teaspoon honey**
- **1 teaspoon rice vinegar**
- **2 scallions, thinly sliced**

1. Combine leeks, water, 2 teaspoons butter, and salt in 6-quart Instant Pot. Sprinkle salmon with 1 teaspoon ginger and soy sauce. Place rack on top of leek mixture; spray rack with nonstick spray. Place salmon on rack, skin side down.
2. Lock lid, making sure vent is closed. Press Steam and set cooking time for 4 minutes. When time is up, press Cancel to turn off pot. Move steam-release valve to Venting position to quickly release pressure. Remove lid.
3. Meanwhile, combine remaining 1 tablespoon butter, remaining 1 teaspoon ginger, miso, honey, and vinegar in small bowl; stir until smooth.
4. Remove salmon with rack from pot. Spread miso mixture over salmon. Cover to keep warm.
5. Press Sauté and set cooking time for 10 minutes. When leeks start to sizzle, cook 5 minutes, stirring occasionally, until leeks are very tender and most of the liquid in pot is evaporated. Press Cancel to turn off pot. Spoon leeks evenly onto 4 serving plates, top with salmon, and sprinkle with scallions.

**Per serving** (1 piece salmon, ⅓ cup leeks, and scant 1 tablespoon miso butter): 402 Cal, 24 g Total Fat, 7 g Sat Fat, 574 mg Sod, 15 g Total Carb, 6 g Sugar, 2 g Fib, 31 g Prot.

# Kimchi soba with shrimp and edamame

**Prep 15 min   Cook 15 min   Serves 4**

7 4 1

Luscious pan-grilled shrimp make a satisfying topping for whole-grain soba noodles mixed with crunchy veggies and tangy, probiotic-rich kimchi. Some kimchis are quite mild, while others pack lots of heat; serve kimchi on the side if you're worried about spiciness.

- **4 ounces soba (100% buckwheat) noodles**
- **1 cup frozen shelled edamame, thawed**
- **1 red bell pepper, thinly sliced**
- **1 orange or yellow bell pepper, thinly sliced**
- **¾ cup kimchi, thinly sliced, plus 2 tablespoons liquid from jar**
- **1 tablespoon Asian (dark) sesame oil**
- **¾ teaspoon salt**
- **1 pound large shrimp, peeled and deveined**
- **½ teaspoon five-spice powder**

**1** Cook noodles according to package directions, adding edamame during last 2 minutes of cooking time; drain. Rinse and drain again. Transfer to large bowl. Add bell peppers, kimchi, oil, and ½ teaspoon salt; toss to coat evenly.

**2** Meanwhile, pat shrimp dry with paper towels. Combine shrimp, five-spice powder, and remaining ¼ teaspoon salt in large bowl; toss to coat. Spray ridged grill pan with nonstick spray and set over medium-high heat. Lightly spray shrimp with nonstick spray. Place shrimp on grill pan and grill just until opaque in center, about 2 minutes per side.

**3** Divide noodle mixture among 4 shallow bowls. Top evenly with shrimp.

**Per serving** (generous 1½ cups noodle mixture and about 6 shrimp): 284 Cal, 8 g Total Fat, 1 g Sat Fat, 1,268 mg Sod, 31 g Total Carb, 5 g Sugar, 4 g Fib, 24 g Prot.

# Tagliatelle with clams and broccoli

**Prep 25 min  Cook 15 min  Serves 4**

4 3 3

Steamed clams are so good—and so easy—over pasta. This dish ups the ante with broccoli, shallots, and fresh (not dried) tagliatelle. Add a little heat by sprinkling in a generous pinch of red pepper flakes along with the broth in step 3.

- **8 ounces fresh tagliatelle, linguine, or fettuccine**
- **2 cups small broccoli florets**
- **1 tablespoon olive oil**
- **2 shallots, finely chopped**
- **3 large garlic cloves, minced**
- **4 pounds littleneck or manila clams, scrubbed**
- **½ cup chicken broth**
- **Grated zest and juice of ½ lemon**
- **¼ teaspoon black pepper**
- **2 tablespoons chopped fresh flat-leaf parsley**

**1** Bring large pot of salted water to boil. Add pasta and broccoli and cook until pasta is tender, about 2 minutes. Drain and transfer to large bowl; cover to keep warm.

**2** Meanwhile, heat oil in 14-inch skillet or Dutch oven over medium heat. Add shallots and cook, stirring frequently, until softened, about 2 minutes. Add garlic and cook, stirring constantly, until fragrant, about 30 seconds longer.

**3** Add clams to skillet and cook 1 minute. Add broth and lemon zest and juice; cook, covered, until clams open, about 8 minutes. Discard any clams that do not open. Add pasta, broccoli, and pepper to clams; cook, tossing, until mixed well and heated through, about 1 minute longer. Divide evenly among 4 large shallow bowls and sprinkle with parsley.

**Per serving** (about 10 clams with 1½ cups pasta and sauce): 219 Cal, 5 g Total Fat, 1 g Sat Fat, 668 mg Sod, 25 g Total Carb, 3 g Sugar, 2 g Fib, 18 g Prot.

## Serving idea

Saucy pasta dishes call for crusty Italian bread, right? A 1-ounce slice per serving won't up the SmartPoints® values by much.

# Freekeh stir-fry bowls

**Prep 20 min  Cook 30 min  Serves 4**

8 6 2

We used a simple fried rice-style preparation for freekeh, a chewy, nutty whole grain. Eggs and lots of colorful veggies mixed in make it a complete one-dish meal. If you can't find freekeh, you can use farro instead.

**1 cup freekeh**
**2½ cups water**
**¼ teaspoon salt**
**4 large eggs**
**4 tablespoons chopped fresh cilantro**
**⅛ teaspoon black pepper**
**4 teaspoons peanut oil**
**3 scallions, sliced**
**3 garlic cloves, minced**
**2 tablespoons minced peeled fresh ginger**
**2 cups sugar snap peas, trimmed and halved**
**2 cups small broccoli florets**
**1 red bell pepper, diced**
**2 tablespoons soy sauce**
**Sriracha, for serving**
**Lime wedges, for serving**

**1** Combine freekeh, water, and ⅛ teaspoon salt in small saucepan and bring to boil over high heat. Reduce heat to low and simmer, covered, until freekeh is tender, about 25 minutes. Drain in colander. Rinse under cold running water until cool; drain again.

**2** Meanwhile, whisk together eggs, 2 tablespoons cilantro, remaining ⅛ teaspoon salt, and black pepper in small bowl. Heat 1 teaspoon oil in wok or large deep skillet over high heat. Add egg mixture and swirl to coat pan; stir-fry until set, about 1 minute. Transfer to small bowl.

**3** Wipe out wok. Heat remaining 3 teaspoons oil in wok over high heat. Add scallions, garlic, and ginger; stir-fry just until fragrant, about 30 seconds. Add snap peas, broccoli, and bell pepper; stir-fry just until snap peas and broccoli turn bright green, about 3 minutes. Reduce heat to medium. Add freekeh and soy sauce; stir-fry until hot, about 2 minutes longer.

**4** Divide freekeh mixture evenly among 4 bowls; top evenly with egg and remaining 2 tablespoons cilantro. Serve with sriracha and lime wedges.

**Per serving** (1½ cups): 324 Cal, 11 g Total Fat, 2 g Sat Fat, 672 mg Sod, 42 g Total Carb, 5 g Sugar, 10 g Fib, 17 g Prot.

## Prep ahead

Cook up the freekeh for this meal a day or two ahead and refrigerate. Just heat it for an extra couple of minutes when you add it to the wok in step 3.

# Lentils and brown rice with turmeric yogurt

**Prep 15 min Cook 30 min Serves 4**

11 7 2

This one-pot meal gives you a tasty combination of legumes and whole-grain rice in just about 30 minutes—thanks to the time-saving help of a pressure cooker! Turmeric-spiced yogurt and chopped cashews bring creamy/crunchy textures and add satisfying protein.

**2 teaspoons olive oil**
**1 medium onion, chopped**
**3 cloves garlic, chopped**
**2 teaspoons ground cumin**
**1 teaspoon ground coriander**
**¾ teaspoon ground allspice**
**½ teaspoon cinnamon**
**3¼ cups water**
**1 cup long-grain brown rice**
**¾ cup brown lentils**
**1¾ teaspoons kosher salt**
**¼ teaspoon red pepper flakes**
**4 cups packed baby spinach (about 5 ounces)**
**½ cup plain fat-free Greek yogurt**
**¼ teaspoon ground turmeric**
**¼ teaspoon grated lemon zest**
**Pinch sugar**
**¼ cup coarsely chopped cashews**
**Lemon wedges, for serving**

1 Press Sauté on 6-quart Instant Pot® and set cooking time for 10 minutes. Heat pot for 3 minutes. Add oil, onion, and garlic and cook, stirring, until softened, about 3 minutes. Stir in cumin, coriander, allspice, and cinnamon. Add water, rice, lentils, salt, and pepper flakes. Scrape up any browned bits from bottom of pot. Press Cancel to turn off pot. Lock lid, making sure vent is closed.

2 Press Pressure Cook and select High Pressure; set cooking time for 20 minutes. When time is up, press Cancel to turn off pot. Move steam-release valve to Venting position to release remaining pressure. Remove lid. Stir in spinach. Let stand until spinach is wilted, 3–5 minutes.

3 Meanwhile, stir together yogurt, turmeric, lemon zest, and sugar in small bowl. Serve lentil mixture with yogurt, cashews, and lemon wedges.

**Per serving** (about 2 cups lentils and rice, 2 tablespoons yogurt, and 1 tablespoon cashews): 400 Cal, 8 g Total Fat, 1 g Sat Fat, 937 mg Sod, 67 g Total Carb, 4 g Sugar, 7 g Fib, 18 g Prot.

## Shopping tip

**If you want to substitute just one ground spice for the four that flavor this stew, pick up a jar of the spice blend garam masala at your supermarket or at an Asian food store.**

# Garlicky kale and bean-stuffed potatoes

**Prep 25 min  Cook 1 hr 10 min  Serves 4**

9 7 2

These hearty double-baked potatoes bring together sweet peppers, onions, earthy kale, and a nice hit of fresh garlic. If your family doesn't love kale, use fresh baby spinach instead and decrease the sautéing time by a few minutes.

- **4 (8-ounce) russet potatoes**
- **2 teaspoons olive oil**
- **1 red bell pepper, thinly sliced**
- **1 medium red onion, halved and sliced into thin wedges**
- **2 teaspoons fresh thyme leaves**
- **3 garlic cloves, sliced**
- **3 cups lightly packed chopped curly kale**
- **1 (15-ounce) can cannellini (white kidney) beans, rinsed and drained**
- **2 tablespoons water**
- **⅓ cup vegetable broth plus additional as need**
- **1 tablespoon unsalted butter**
- **¾ teaspoon salt**
- **½ teaspoon black pepper**

**1** Preheat oven to 400°F.

**2** Scrub potatoes, pat dry, and prick each several times with fork; place on small rimmed baking sheet. Bake until potatoes are very soft when pierced with tip of paring knife, about 1 hour. Leave oven on.

**3** Meanwhile, heat oil in large skillet over medium heat. Add bell pepper, onion, thyme, and garlic. Cook, stirring frequently, until vegetables are very soft, about 10 minutes. Add kale and cook, stirring, until wilted, about 5 minutes, adding tablespoon or two of water if mixture seems dry. Set aside.

**4** Set aside ½ cup beans. Place remaining beans in food processor with water and process until smooth. Transfer to medium bowl.

**5** When potatoes are cool enough to handle, slice each potato in half lengthwise. Scoop out potato flesh, leaving ¼-inch wall. Reserve half of potato flesh (about 1½ cups) for another use. Place remaining potato flesh in bowl with pureed beans. With fork, mash beans and potato together. Stir in broth, butter, ½ teaspoon salt, and ¼ teaspoon pepper. Spoon mixture evenly into potato shells. Place filled potatoes on small baking sheet.

**6** Stir kale mixture, reserved whole beans, and remaining ¼ teaspoon salt and ¼ teaspoon pepper in bowl. Pile kale mixture into potatoes. Place sheet of foil loosely over potatoes. Bake until heated through, 8–10 minutes.

**Per serving** (2 stuffed potato halves): 330 Cal, 6 g Total Fat, 2 g Sat Fat, 869 mg Sod, 61 g Total Carb, 4 g Sugar, 8 g Fib, 12 g Prot.

# Smoky bean and barley burgers

**Prep 25 min Cook 45 min Serves 6**

5 3 1

These grain-based burgers check the boxes for hearty taste and texture. You can opt to serve them in buns if you'd like, or place them on crisp lettuce leaves and top with a dollop of your favorite salsa and cooling Greek yogurt mixed with a little lime juice.

**½ cup pearl barley, rinsed**
**1 poblano pepper, finely chopped**
**1 small onion, finely chopped**
**1 cup thawed frozen corn kernels**
**2 garlic cloves, crushed through a press**
**1 teaspoon smoked paprika**
**¼ teaspoon ground chipotle chile powder**
**1 (15½-ounce) can pinto beans, rinsed and drained**
**⅓ cup chopped fresh cilantro**
**1 large egg, lightly beaten**
**3 tablespoons grated Parmesan**
**¾ teaspoon salt**
**2 teaspoons canola oil**

**1** Bring medium pot of salted water to boil; stir in barley. Reduce heat and simmer until tender, about 35 minutes. Drain well and spread on large plate to cool.

**2** Meanwhile, spray large heavy skillet with nonstick spray and set over medium heat. Add poblano, onion, and corn and cook, stirring occasionally, until vegetables begin to brown, about 10 minutes. Add garlic, paprika, and chile powder; cook, stirring constantly, until fragrant, about 30 seconds. Transfer to plate to cool. (Do not wash skillet.)

**3** Place beans in food processor and pulse to coarsely chop. Transfer beans to large bowl; add barley, poblano mixture, cilantro, egg, Parmesan, and salt, stirring to combine. Transfer 1½ cups mixture to food processor. Process until finely chopped but not completely smooth. Return mixture to bowl and stir to mix well.

**4** Divide bean mixture into 6 equal portions, using about ½ cup for each. Shape each into ball and then press to form 4-inch patties (shaping mixture into ball helps hold it together).

**5** Wipe out skillet; add oil and set over medium heat. When hot, add burgers, in batches if necessary, and cook until well browned, about 5 minutes per side.

**Per serving** (1 burger): 191 Cal, 4 g Total Fat, 1 g Sat Fat, 560 mg Sod, 32 g Total Carb, 3 g Sugar, 7 g Fib, 8 g Prot.

## Prep ahead

A stash of these burgers in your freezer will give you a fast lunch or dinner on busy days. To freeze them, place in a zip-close plastic bag with a layer of parchment or wax paper between each. To reheat, wrap a frozen burger loosely in a paper towel and microwave on High until heated through, 60 to 90 seconds.

# Jackfruit tacos with sriracha mayo

**Prep 20 min  Cook 30 min  Serves 4**

8 7 7

When it's ripe, jackfruit has a rich tropical flavor that's like a cross between pineapple and banana. Unripe fruit is firmer and less sweet and makes a popular vegan meat substitute. These tacos call for convenient canned jackfruit in brine, available at many larger supermarkets.

- **1 (20-ounce) can green jackfruit in brine, drained**
- **3 teaspoons canola oil**
- **½ medium onion, finely diced**
- **2 garlic cloves, finely chopped**
- **2 teaspoons chili powder**
- **½ teaspoon dried oregano**
- **1 teaspoon ground cumin**
- **¾ teaspoon salt**
- **1½ tablespoons tomato paste**
- **½ cup water**
- **1 cup black beans, rinsed and drained**
- **¼ teaspoon ancho chile powder**
- **2 tablespoons vegan mayonnaise**
- **2 teaspoons lime juice**
- **¾ teaspoon sriracha**
- **8 corn tortillas, warmed**
- **1 Hass avocado, pitted, peeled, and thinly sliced**
- **½ cup shredded red cabbage**
- **Fresh cilantro leaves, for garnish**

**1** To prepare jackfruit, cutting with grain, thinly slice pieces, then shred with your fingers. Heat 2 teaspoons oil in large skillet over medium heat. Add onion and garlic and cook, stirring often, until softened, about 5 minutes. Stir in chili powder, oregano, ½ teaspoon cumin, and ½ teaspoon salt; cook until fragrant, about 1 minute. Stir in jackfruit, tomato paste, and water. Bring to boil; reduce heat, cover, and simmer until jackfruit is very soft, about 25 minutes.

**2** Meanwhile, stir together beans, ancho chile powder, remaining 1 teaspoon oil, remaining ½ teaspoon cumin, and remaining ¼ teaspoon salt in small microwavable bowl. Cover with paper towel and microwave on High until very hot, 1–2 minutes, stirring beans every 30 seconds. Keep warm.

**3** Stir together mayonnaise, lime juice, and sriracha in cup. Fill tortillas with jackfruit and top evenly with beans, avocado, and cabbage. Drizzle each with about 1 teaspoon sriracha mayonnaise and top each with a few cilantro leaves.

**Per serving** (2 tacos): 341 Cal, 12 g Total Fat, 2 g Sat Fat, 1,140 mg Sod, 53 g Total Carb, 3 g Sugar, 18 g Fib, 8 g Prot.

## Prep ahead

Want to make some of the elements of these tacos in advance? You can make both the jackfruit filling and the beans up to 2 days ahead and refrigerate them. Reheat in the microwave just before serving.

# Spelt spaghetti with broccoli rabe

**Prep 15 min Cook 25 min Serves 4**

Here's a classic Italian pasta dish with a healthy twist. Spelt is an ancient grain that originated more than 8,000 years ago. Pastas made from it are higher in protein than those made from wheat and have a mild, nutty flavor. Look for it online and in specialty stores.

- **6 ounces spelt spaghetti or whole-wheat spaghetti**
- **1 bunch broccoli rabe, trimmed and cut into 1-inch pieces**
- **1 tablespoon olive oil**
- **3 garlic cloves, thinly sliced**
- **⅛ teaspoon pepperoncino flakes or red pepper flakes, or to taste**
- **3 anchovy fillets, drained and minced**
- **¼ teaspoon salt**
- **¼ cup shaved ricotta salata**

**1** Cook pasta according to package directions, adding broccoli rabe during last 2 minutes of cooking time. Drain pasta and broccoli rabe, reserving ¼ cup cooking liquid.

**2** Meanwhile, heat oil in large deep skillet over medium heat. Add garlic and pepperoncino flakes; cook, stirring constantly, just until garlic turns pale golden, about 1 minute. Add anchovies and cook, stirring frequently, until anchovies soften and mixture is fragrant, about 1 minute longer.

**3** Add pasta mixture and salt to skillet and cook, stirring constantly, just until heated through, 1–2 minutes, adding reserved cooking liquid if mixture seems dry. Divide pasta evenly among 4 plates and sprinkle evenly with ricotta salata. Sprinkle with additional pepperoncino flakes, if desired.

**Per serving** (1¼ cups pasta and 1 tablespoon ricotta salata): 258 Cal, 8 g Total Fat, 3 g Sat Fat, 426 mg Sod, 36 g Total Carb, 8 g Sugar, 5 g Fib, 14 g Prot.

## Shopping tip

Pepperoncino comes from dried chiles grown in southern Italy's Calabria region. The flakes are prized for their heat and fruity flavor. Look for it online or in specialty markets, or substitute regular red pepper flakes.

# Stuffed pasta shells

**Prep 25 min  Cook 40 min  Serves 6**

9 9 9

This classic dish of marinara-coated pasta filled with ricotta, cottage cheese, and garlic is perfect for a family meal, potluck dinner, or casual dinner party.

- **6 ounces (about 24) jumbo pasta shells**
- **1¼ cups part-skim ricotta**
- **1¼ cups low-fat cottage cheese**
- **1 large egg, beaten**
- **1 garlic clove, minced**
- **2 tablespoons finely chopped fresh parsley**
- **1 teaspoon dried oregano**
- **½ teaspoon salt, or to taste**
- **¼ teaspoon black pepper**
- **2½ cups marinara sauce**
- **¼ cup grated Parmesan**

**1** Bring large saucepan filled two-thirds full of salted water to boil. Add shells, reduce heat, and simmer until shells are just tender, about 10 minutes. Drain well, shaking strainer to remove as much water as possible; let cool slightly.

**2** Preheat oven to 375°F. Spray 7 x 11-inch baking dish or 2-quart gratin dish with nonstick spray.

**3** Meanwhile, stir together ricotta, cottage cheese, egg, garlic, parsley, oregano, salt, and pepper in large bowl.

**4** Spread about ¾ cup marinara in prepared dish. Spoon ricotta mixture evenly into shells, filling each one just barely full. Arrange in baking dish, filled side up. Spoon remaining marinara over top and sprinkle evenly with Parmesan. Bake until sauce is bubbling, about 20 minutes.

**Per serving** (4 stuffed shells and sauce): 301 Cal, 9 g Total Fat, 4 g Sat Fat, 954 mg Sod, 35 g Total Carb, 7 g Sugar, 3 g Fib, 19 g Prot.

## Smart pointers

Sauté broccoli florets, red bell pepper strips, and garlic in a skillet sprayed with nonstick spray to make a 5-minute, 0 SmartPoints® side dish.

# Zucchini ribbons with herb pesto

**Prep 20 min   Cook 0 min   Serves 4**

3 3 3

Here's a fresh, no-cook take on zucchini and tomatoes. Zucchini ribbons are topped with ripe tomatoes, dotted with a fresh herb pesto, and then sprinkled with Parmesan. If you don't want to use multiple kinds of herbs, go with 2½ cups of fresh basil leaves for a classically delicious sauce.

- **1 pound regular, heirloom, or plum tomatoes**
- **1 cup lightly packed fresh basil leaves**
- **½ cup lightly packed fresh flat-leaf parsley leaves**
- **½ cup lightly packed fresh cilantro leaves**
- **¼ cup lightly packed fresh mint leaves**
- **¼ cup chopped fresh chives**
- **1 garlic clove, grated on Microplane grater or minced**
- **¼ cup water**
- **4 teaspoons extra-virgin olive oil**
- **4 tablespoons grated Parmesan**
- **½ teaspoon salt**
- **¼ teaspoon black pepper, plus additional for serving**
- **4 (6-ounce) zucchini or yellow squash**

**1** Cut tomatoes into ¼-inch dice; place in sieve set over medium bowl to allow tomato water to drain. Reserve tomato water.

**2** Meanwhile, to make pesto, combine basil, parsley, cilantro, mint, chives, garlic, and water in food processor and pulse until finely chopped. With machine running, add oil and process until mixture forms coarse puree. Pour into small bowl and stir in 2 tablespoons Parmesan, salt, and ¼ teaspoon pepper. Thin with reserved tomato water to make saucy consistency, if needed. Press piece of plastic wrap directly onto surface of pesto to prevent browning. Set aside.

**3** To make zucchini ribbons, with mandoline, V-slicer, or sharp vegetable peeler, shave thin lengthwise ribbons from zucchini, stopping when you reach seedy center.

**4** To assemble, loosely pile zucchini ribbons onto each of 4 plates. Scatter tomatoes over zucchini and top each serving with 2 tablespoons pesto, ½ tablespoon Parmesan, and a few pinches of pepper. Serve remaining pesto alongside or refrigerate in airtight container up to 1 week.

**Per serving** (2 cups zucchini with about ½ cup tomato, 2 tablespoons pesto, and ½ tablespoon Parmesan): 124 Cal, 7 g Total Fat, 2 g Sat Fat, 429 mg Sod, 12 g Total Carb, 7 g Sugar, 4 g Fib, 6 g Prot.

Chapter 4

# Desserts

START WITH THE BASE

## 2-ingredient banana nice cream

**Prep 10 min Freezing time 2-3 hrs Serves 4**

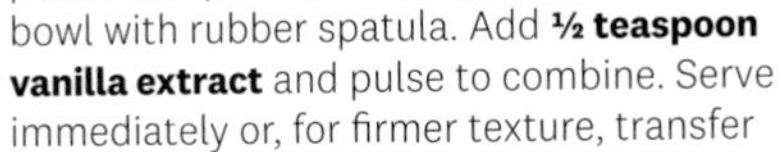

Peel **4 ripe large bananas;** cut into 1-inch chunks and place in large zip-close plastic freezer bag. Seal and freeze until frozen solid, 2-3 hours. Place bananas in food processor; puree, scraping down side of bowl with rubber spatula. Add **½ teaspoon vanilla extract** and pulse to combine. Serve immediately or, for firmer texture, transfer to container and freeze until ready to serve; allow to soften about 10 minutes at room temperature. Garnish with banana slices. Per serving: ½ cup

SOME NICE CREAM COMBOS WE LOVE

## Chocolate-almond nice cream

**Prep 10 min Freezing time 2-3 hrs Serves 4**

Make 2-Ingredient banana nice cream. Use rubber spatula to stir **¼ cup semisweet mini-chocolate chips** into pureed mixture, then top each serving with **½ tablespoon sliced toasted almonds.** Per serving: ½ cup

## Peanut butter-banana nice cream

**Prep 10 min Freezing time 2-3 hrs Serves 4**

Make 2-Ingredient banana nice cream, adding **3 tablespoons smooth peanut butter** to food processor along with vanilla. Top each serving with **½ tablespoon chopped roasted salted peanuts.** Per serving: ½ cup

## Strawberry nice cream

**Prep 10 min Freezing time 2-3 hrs Serves 4**

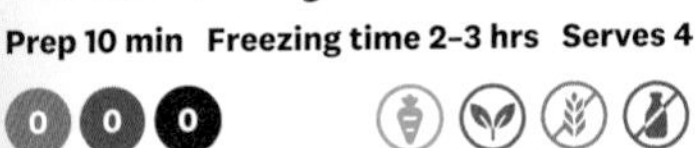

Make 2-Ingredient banana nice cream, substituting **1½ cups unsweetened frozen sliced strawberries** for 2 of the bananas. Garnish each serving with a few **fresh berries** and **mint sprigs,** if desired. Per serving: ½ cup

### Chocolate-almond nice cream

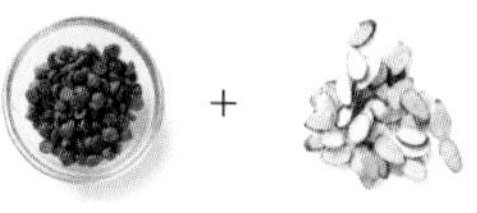

### Peanut butter-banana nice cream

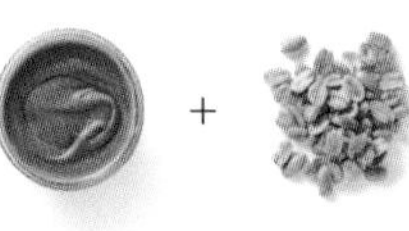

### Strawberry nice cream

## Lemon-berry pizzelle tart

**Prep 5 min Cook 0 min Serves 1**

Stir together **2 tablespoons natural whipped topping, 2 teaspoons lemon curd, ¼ teaspoon grated lemon zest,** and **¼ teaspoon lemon juice** in cup; spread mixture over **1 (3- to 4-inch) lemon pizzelle cookie.** Top with **mixed fresh berries.**

## Chocolate-citrus pizzelle tart

**Prep 5 min Cook 0 min Serves 1**

Spread **2 tablespoons natural whipped topping** onto **1 (3- to 4-inch) chocolate pizzelle cookie.** Place on plate and top with **2 peeled slices or sections of pink grapefruit** and **2 peeled slices or sections of orange;** sprinkle with **½ tablespoon shaved semisweet chocolate.**

## Chocolate-peanut butter pizzelle tart

**Prep 5 min Cook 0 min Serves 1**

Whisk together **1½ teaspoons chocolate peanut butter powder** and **2¼ teaspoons water** in small bowl; stir in **3 tablespoons natural whipped topping.** Spread onto **1 (3- to 4-inch) chocolate pizzelle cookie;** top with about **8 thin slices banana** and sprinkle with **1 teaspoon mini chocolate chips.**

## White chocolate-blueberry pizzelle tart

**Prep 5 min Cook 0 min Serves 1**

Place **1 tablespoon white chocolate chips** in small zip-close plastic bag; seal and microwave on High, about 20 seconds, stopping and kneading chocolate every 5 seconds, until melted. Snip small corner from bag; drizzle chocolate over **1 (3- to 4-inch) chocolate pizzelle.** Sprinkle with **2 tablespoons blueberries** and **2 teaspoons toasted unsweetened flaked coconut.**

**Chocolate-citrus pizzelle tart**

**Chocolate-peanut butter pizzelle tart**

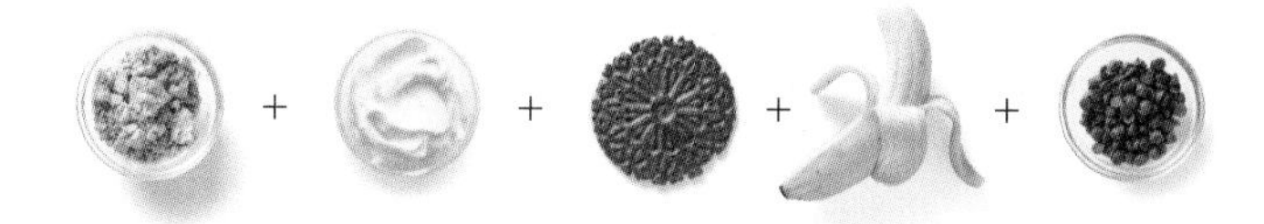

**White chocolate-blueberry pizzelle tart**

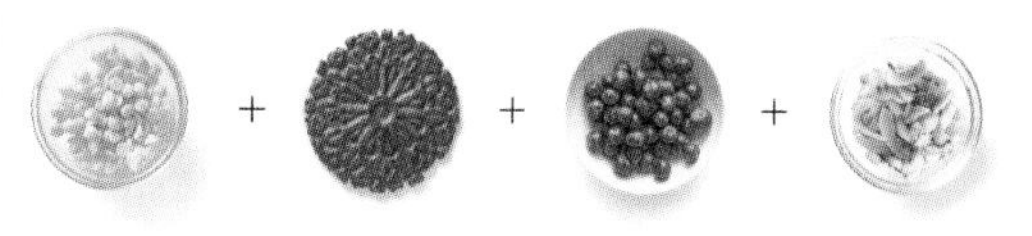

# Decadent avocado-chocolate cake

**Prep 20 min  Cook 30 min  Serves 16**

5 5 5

Ready to venture beyond avocado toast? Get a dose of heart-healthy omega-3s from a rich, dark, totally satisfying cake that replaces refined fat with avocado. How to keep leftover avocado from browning and turning slimy? Leave the pit in, cover in plastic or reusable food wrap, and refrigerate.

- **3 ounces semisweet chocolate, chopped**
- **1 cup all-purpose flour**
- **½ cup unsweetened cocoa powder**
- **¾ cup granulated sugar**
- **1 teaspoon baking powder**
- **¾ teaspoon baking soda**
- **⅛ teaspoon salt**
- **1 cup plain low-fat yogurt**
- **½ ripe Hass avocado, pitted, peeled, and chopped**
- **1 large egg**
- **1 teaspoon vanilla extract**
- **1 teaspoon confectioners' sugar**

**1** Preheat oven to 350°F. Line bottom of 8-inch round cake pan with parchment paper; spray paper and side of pan with nonstick spray.

**2** Place chocolate in medium microwavable bowl and microwave on Low until melted, stirring every 20 seconds. Let cool slightly.

**3** Stir together flour, cocoa powder, granulated sugar, baking powder, baking soda, and salt in large bowl.

**4** Place yogurt in blender; add avocado and puree. Add egg and vanilla and pulse just until combined. Add avocado mixture and melted chocolate to flour mixture and stir until smooth. Spoon batter into prepared pan, smoothing the top. Bake until toothpick inserted into center comes out clean, 28–30 minutes.

**5** Cool cake in pan on wire rack 10 minutes. Remove cake from pan and let cool completely, right side up, on wire rack. Dust with confectioners' sugar just before serving. Cut into 16 slices.

**Per serving** (1 slice): 120 Cal, 3 g Total Fat, 1 g Sat Fat, 124 mg Sod, 22 g Total Carb, 14 g Sugar, 2 g Fib, 3 g Prot.

## Smart pointers

Top the cake with mint leaves or fresh raspberries for a splash of color and 0 additional SmartPoints®.

# Banana-chocolate chip mini muffins

**Prep 20 min  Cook 17 min  Serves 24**

Naturally sweet banana lets us use less sugar and makes these two-bite muffins moist. Oats add fiber and texture, and chocolate chips make them crowd-pleasers.

- **⅔ cup plain low-fat Greek yogurt**
- **⅓ cup low-fat (1%) milk**
- **1 large egg**
- **½ cup quick-cooking oats**
- **⅓ cup packed brown sugar**
- **1 ripe banana, mashed**
- **1½ teaspoons vanilla extract**
- **½ cup all-purpose flour**
- **⅓ cup whole-wheat flour**
- **1¼ teaspoons baking powder**
- **½ teaspoon baking soda**
- **½ teaspoon salt**
- **½ cup semisweet mini chocolate chips**

**1** Preheat oven to 375°F. Spray 24-cup mini-muffin pan with nonstick spray.

**2** Whisk together yogurt, milk, and egg in large bowl. Add oats, brown sugar, banana, and vanilla, whisking to combine; let stand 5 minutes.

**3** Meanwhile, whisk together all-purpose flour, whole-wheat flour, baking powder, baking soda, and salt in medium bowl. Add flour mixture and all but 1 tablespoon chocolate chips to yogurt mixture, stirring until moistened.

**4** Spoon batter evenly into prepared muffin cups; sprinkle evenly with reserved chocolate chips.

**5** Bake until golden brown on top and toothpick inserted into center of muffin comes out clean, 15–17 minutes. Let cool in pan on wire rack 5 minutes; run knife around inside of cups to loosen muffins from pan. Remove from pan and cool completely on rack. Store in airtight container at room temperature up to 2 days or freeze up to 3 months.

**Per serving** (1 muffin): 71 Cal, 2 g Total Fat, 1 g Sat Fat, 108 mg Sod, 11 g Total Carb, 6 g Sugar, 1 g Fib, 2 g Prot.

# Frozen chocolate chip–peanut butter pie

**Prep 20 min Freezing time 4 hr Serves 12**

If you don't know powdered peanut butter yet, this pie is a great introduction. Made from pure roasted peanuts, the powder packs big nutty flavor with much less fat, and it's easy to incorporate into other ingredients.

- **¾ cup + 2 tablespoons powdered peanut butter**
- **½ cup + ⅓ cup ice water**
- **6 tablespoons plain fat-free Greek yogurt**
- **6 tablespoons confectioners' sugar**
- **¼ teaspoon salt**
- **⅓ cup instant nonfat dry milk**
- **1 pasteurized egg white (2 tablespoons)**
- **1 teaspoon lemon juice**
- **1¼ teaspoons vanilla extract**
- **7 tablespoons semisweet mini chocolate chips**
- **1 (6-ounce) prepared graham cracker crust**

**1** Stir together powdered peanut butter and ½ cup ice water in medium bowl until smooth. Stir in yogurt, 3 tablespoons confectioners' sugar, and salt. Set aside.

**2** Combine dry milk, remaining ⅓ cup ice water, and egg white in large bowl and beat with electric mixer on high speed until mixture is very thick, 3–4 minutes, stopping once or twice to scrape down side of bowl. Beat in remaining 3 tablespoons confectioners' sugar, one tablespoon at a time. Beat in lemon juice and vanilla. Continue beating until mixture is very thick and light (it should be the consistency of sour cream).

**3** Gently stir dry milk mixture into powdered peanut butter mixture. Fold in 3 tablespoons chocolate chips. Spoon mixture into crust and spread evenly; sprinkle with remaining 4 tablespoons chocolate chips. Cover with plastic wrap and freeze until completely frozen, at least 4 hours or up to 2 days. Let pie soften at room temperature 15 minutes before serving. Cut into 12 wedges.

**Per serving** (1 wedge): 166 Cal, 7 g Total Fat, 3 g Sat Fat, 191 mg Sod, 20 g Total Carb, 13 g Sugar, 2 g Fib, 5 g Prot.

## Shopping tip

Use pasteurized egg whites in dishes that aren't cooked, like this pie, to reduce the risk of food-borne illness. They are sold in larger supermarkets, in cartons or sometimes in the shell.

# Two-bite Key lime tarts

**Prep 10 min   Cook 5 min   Serves 15**

2 2 2

These citrusy mini dessert treats are superquick to prepare. If you don't have a zester for the garnish, use a Microplane grater or the small holes on a box grater.

**15 mini phyllo shells (1.9-ounce box)**

**4 ounces light cream cheese (Neufchâtel)**

**3 tablespoons plain low-fat Greek yogurt**

**3 tablespoons sugar**

**1½ tablespoons Key lime or regular (Persian) lime juice**

**¾ teaspoon vanilla extract**

**Zest of 2 limes, removed in strips with citrus zester or grated**

**2 tablespoons toasted sliced almonds**

**1** Preheat oven to 350°F. Place phyllo shells on small baking sheet and bake until crisp, about 5 minutes. Transfer shells to wire rack and let cool.

**2** Meanwhile, combine cream cheese and yogurt in medium bowl. Beat with electric mixer on medium speed until smooth. Beat in sugar, lime juice, vanilla, and half of lime zest. Spoon or pipe mixture into phyllo cups. Garnish each tart with lime zest and a few sliced almonds. Serve immediately.

**Per serving** (1 tart): 53 Cal, 3 g Total Fat, 1 g Sat Fat, 36 mg Sod, 6 g Total Carb, 3 g Sugar, 0 g Fib, 2 g Prot.

## Prep ahead

**You can make the filling up to 2 days ahead, but fill the tarts just before serving so they stay crisp.**

# Butternut brownies

**Prep 20 min   Cook 20 min   Serves 16**

4 4 4

Vitamin-rich butternut squash boosts flavor and cuts fat in these fantastically fudgy brownies. Got leftover squash puree? Let it work its sweet-and-healthy magic in other dishes: Add it to a cheese sauce for broccoli, stir it into bean soup for richness, or add a few spoonfuls to muffin batter.

- **3 ounces semisweet chocolate, chopped**
- **¾ cup all-purpose flour**
- **¼ cup unsweetened cocoa powder**
- **¾ teaspoon baking powder**
- **¼ teaspoon salt**
- **½ cup thawed frozen winter squash puree**
- **⅓ cup pure maple syrup**
- **4 tablespoons unsalted butter, melted and cooled**
- **1 large egg**
- **1 teaspoon vanilla extract**

**1** Preheat oven to 350°F. Line 8-inch square baking pan with foil, allowing foil to extend over rim of pan by 2 inches; spray foil with nonstick spray.

**2** Place chocolate in medium microwavable bowl and microwave on Low until melted, stirring every 20 seconds. Let cool slightly.

**3** Stir together flour, cocoa powder, baking powder, and salt in medium bowl. Set aside.

**4** Stir together squash, maple syrup, butter, egg, and vanilla in small bowl until blended. Add squash mixture to flour mixture; stir until flour mixture is just moistened. Stir in melted chocolate until blended. Spoon batter into prepared pan and spread evenly. Bake until brownies spring back when lightly touched in center, about 20 minutes (do not overbake).

**5** Cool brownies completely in pan on wire rack. Lift from pan using foil as handles. Peel away foil from brownies. Cut into 16 squares.

**Per serving** (1 brownie): 101 Cal, 5 g Total Fat, 3 g Sat Fat, 66 mg Sod, 14 g Total Carb, 7 g Sugar, 1 g Fib, 2 g Prot.

## Prep ahead

**If you're not planning to serve all the brownies, stash some in the freezer to help prevent the temptation to go back for seconds or thirds. Wrap individual brownies in plastic wrap and store them together in a zip-close freezer bag. Thaw at room temperature or unwrap each brownie and microwave about 20 seconds.**

# Orange–cream cheese cookie cups

**Prep 30 min Cook 20 min Serves 24**

3 3 3

Whole-wheat pastry flour offers the best of both worlds: It's ground from 100% whole wheat so it packs all the nutrients (like B vitamins) of regular whole-wheat flour, but its lower protein content makes for tender, light-textured baked goods like these irresistible cookies.

- **1 (8-ounce) package light cream cheese (Neufchâtel), softened**
- **2 tablespoons unsalted butter, softened**
- **3 tablespoons low-fat (1%) milk**
- **1 tablespoon + ⅓ cup granulated sugar**
- **¾ cup all-purpose flour**
- **¼ cup whole-wheat pastry flour**
- **⅛ teaspoon salt**
- **1 large egg**
- **2 teaspoons grated orange zest**
- **1 tablespoon orange juice**
- **1 teaspoon vanilla extract**
- **24 fresh raspberries**
- **1 teaspoon confectioners' sugar**

**1** Preheat oven to 350°F. Spray 24-cup mini-muffin pan with nonstick spray.

**2** To make cookie dough, combine ¼ cup cream cheese and butter in medium bowl; beat with electric mixer on medium speed until smooth. Add milk and 1 tablespoon granulated sugar; beat until blended. Add all-purpose flour, pastry flour, and salt, stirring until moist clumps form. Knead dough in bowl 4 times to form ball.

**3** Divide dough into 24 pieces (about 1 heaping teaspoon each). Roll 1 piece of dough into ball and use fingers to shape into 2-inch round. Press into bottom and against side of prepared muffin cup. Repeat with remaining pieces of dough.

**4** To prepare filling, combine remaining cream cheese, remaining ⅓ cup granulated sugar, egg, orange zest and juice, and vanilla in food processor; pulse until smooth.

**5** Spoon 2 teaspoons filling into each dough cup. Bake until filling is set and edges of crust are golden, 18–20 minutes. With tip of small knife or with narrow metal spatula, lift out each cookie cup and let cool completely on wire rack. Top each cup with a raspberry. Place confectioners' sugar in small sieve and sprinkle over cookies.

**Per serving** (1 cookie cup): 71 Cal, 3 g Total Fat, 2 g Sat Fat, 48 mg Sod, 8 g Total Carb, 4 g Sugar, 0 g Fib, 2 g Prot.

## Shopping tip

**Look for whole-wheat pastry flour in larger supermarkets or in health-food stores. Keep in an airtight container up to 3 months, or freeze it up to 6 months.**

# Coconut-chocolate bonbons

**Prep 30 min  Freezing time 6 hr  Serves 24**

Toasting coconut flakes not only intensifies their flavor, but gives them a crunchy texture and a soft brown color. For even toasting, use the oven rather than a skillet, and bake them at 325°F for about 6 minutes, stirring once.

- **1 cup sweetened flaked coconut, toasted**
- **1½ pints vanilla light ice cream**
- **3 ounces semisweet chocolate, chopped**

**1** Line small baking sheet with wax paper or parchment paper; place in freezer 1 hour ahead.

**2** Spread coconut on separate sheet of wax paper or parchment paper.

**3** Using mini ice-cream scoop or teaspoon, scoop ice cream by tablespoonful to form ball; quickly roll in coconut, lightly pressing coconut into ice cream so it adheres. Transfer bonbon to baking sheet in freezer. Repeat with remaining ice cream and coconut, making total of 24 bonbons. Freeze at least 6 hours or up to overnight (if freezing overnight, cover with foil).

**4** Up to 4 hours before serving, place chocolate in medium microwavable bowl and microwave on Low until melted, stirring every 20 seconds. Let cool slightly.

**5** Remove bonbons from freezer. Drizzle chocolate over bonbons in zigzag pattern. Return bonbons to freezer until chocolate is set. Arrange bonbons on platter or place in mini baking cups.

**Per serving** (1 bonbon): 74 Cal, 3 g Total Fat, 2 g Sat Fat, 25 mg Sod, 10 g Total Carb, 8 g Sugar, 1 g Fib, 1 g Prot.

## Prep ahead

**Once the chocolate drizzle is set, you can transfer the bonbons to an airtight container and place back in the freezer; they'll keep for up to a month.**

# Cinnamon rice pudding with coconut

**Prep 15 min Cook 2–5 hr Serves 6**

8 8 8

What makes rice pudding one of the all-time favorite comfort foods? Must be the combo of its creamy texture, luxurious taste, and smell of vanilla. This easy version is made in a slow cooker, so you don't have to tend to it while it cooks.

- **4 tablespoons sweetened flaked coconut or toasted coconut chips**
- **¼ cup sugar**
- **4 cups low-fat (1%) milk**
- **½ cup Arborio rice**
- **½ teaspoon grated orange zest**
- **¼ teaspoon cinnamon, plus more for serving**
- **⅛ teaspoon ground nutmeg**
- **2 teaspoons vanilla extract**
- **¼ teaspoon coconut extract**

**1** Chop 2 tablespoons coconut and transfer to 4-quart slow cooker. Combine sugar and ½ cup milk in small microwavable bowl. Microwave on High until milk is steaming hot, about 1 minute. Stir until sugar is dissolved.

**2** Pour milk mixture into slow cooker. Add remaining 3½ cups milk, rice, orange zest, ¼ teaspoon cinnamon, and nutmeg, stirring to mix well. Cover and cook until rice is tender, about 2 hours on High or 5 hours on Low. Stir in vanilla and coconut extracts.

**3** Divide rice pudding evenly among 6 dessert dishes. Sprinkle with remaining 2 tablespoons coconut and a little more cinnamon. Can be served warm or chilled.

**Per serving** (about ½ cup pudding and 1 teaspoon coconut): 185 Cal, 3 g Total Fat, 2 g Sat Fat, 82 mg Sod, 32 g Total Carb, 18 g Sugar, 1 g Fib, 7 g Prot.

## Serving idea

**Layer your rice pudding with berries or chopped fresh fruit to turn it into an even yummier dessert, for 0 additional SmartPoints®.**

# Pears in port wine

**Prep 20 min  Cook 3 hr 15 min  Chill 4 hr  Serves 6**

5 5 5

Bosc pears are a great choice for poaching because their flesh is firmer than other varieties, so they keep their shape even with long cooking times. Poaching the pears in a slow cooker is easy and deepens the flavors.

**6 Bosc pears with stems, peeled**
**2 teaspoons lemon juice**
**⅔ cup ruby port**
**½ cup packed brown sugar**
**Pinch salt**
**4 cups water**
**1 (3-inch) cinnamon stick**

**1** Brush pears with lemon juice to prevent browning; place on their sides in 5- or 6-quart slow cooker. Whisk together port, brown sugar, and salt in small bowl. Add to slow cooker along with water and cinnamon stick. Cover and cook until pears are tender when pierced in stem end with small sharp knife, 2½–3 hours on Low, gently turning pears over halfway through cooking time.

**2** With slotted spoon, carefully transfer pears to covered container. Pour cooking liquid into large saucepan and bring to boil over high heat. Boil, swirling pan occasionally, until reduced to ¾ cup, 12–15 minutes (sauce will be consistency of light syrup). Transfer sauce to separate covered container. Let pears and sauce cool completely. Cover and refrigerate at least 4 hours or up to 3 days.

**3** Place pears on 6 dessert plates. Top evenly with sauce.

**Per serving** (1 pear and about 2 tablespoons sauce): 213 Cal, 0 g Total Fat, 0 g Sat Fat, 62 mg Sod, 48 g Total Carb, 36 g Sugar, 6 g Fib, 1 g Prot.

## Serving idea

**Though it will no longer be dairy-free, consider serving a ¼-cup dollop of plain low-fat Greek yogurt alongside the pears and sauce.**

# Autumn fruit with maple-yogurt topping

**Prep 15 min  Cook 10 min  Serves 4**

2 2 2

Classic fall flavors make this simple fruit-based recipe a just-right dessert or even a brunch side dish. The yogurt topping is low in SmartPoints®—and takes just minutes to prepare!

- **2 medium Granny Smith apples, cored and cut into ½-inch pieces**
- **2 medium Bosc or Bartlett pears, cored and cut into ½-inch pieces**
- **1 tablespoon light brown sugar**
- **¾ teaspoon cinnamon**
- **4 medium ripe plums, halved, pitted, and sliced**
- **1 cup plain low-fat Greek yogurt**
- **1 tablespoon maple syrup**
- **1 teaspoon finely grated lemon zest**
- **1 teaspoon vanilla extract**

**1** Spray large heavy nonstick skillet with nonstick spray and place over medium-high heat. In medium bowl, toss apples and pears with brown sugar and ½ teaspoon cinnamon. Add fruit mixture to skillet and cook, stirring frequently, until fruit starts to soften and brown, about 5 minutes. Add plums and cook until fruit is very soft, 4–5 minutes more.

**2** Meanwhile, in small bowl, stir together yogurt, maple syrup, lemon zest, vanilla, and remaining ¼ teaspoon cinnamon. Divide fruit among bowls or plates and top each with a dollop of yogurt topping.

**Per serving** (1 cup fruit and ¼ cup topping): 193 Cal, 1 g Total Fat, 1 g Sat Fat, 24 mg Sod, 40 g Total Carb, 29 g Sugar, 6 g Fib, 7 g Prot.

## Prep ahead

This light fruit dessert is delicious warm, room temperature, or chilled, so it's ideal for making ahead. Both the fruit and the yogurt will keep refrigerated up to 3 days; you can reheat the fruit in the microwave for a warm version.

Chapter 5

# Snacks

# Easy home-popped popcorn | Recipe builder

START WITH THE BASE

## DIY microwave popcorn

**Prep 2 min Cook 3 min Serves 4**

Mix together **¼ cup plain popcorn kernels** and **½ teaspoon canola oil** in large microwavable bowl. Cover with heavy microwavable plate. Put bowl in microwave and cook on High until popping sounds slow to about 5 seconds apart, 2½–3 minutes. (A few kernels may remain unpopped, but cooking popcorn longer may result in scorching some kernels.) Carefully lift off plate as popcorn will be hot. Makes about 8 cups. Per serving: 2 cups

SOME POPCORN MIXES WE LOVE

## Parmesan popcorn with lemon and thyme

**Prep 3 min Cook 0 min Serves 4**

Lightly spray **8 cups popcorn** with olive oil nonstick spray, tossing as you spray. Sprinkle with **¼ cup grated Parmesan cheese, 1 tablespoon chopped fresh thyme, grated zest of ½ lemon,** and **¼ teaspoon black pepper.** Toss until mixed well. Per serving: 2 cups

## Everything-bagel popcorn

**Prep 1 min Cook 0 min Serves 4**

Spread **8 cups popcorn** on large rimmed baking sheet. Mix together **2 teaspoons granulated onion, 2 teaspoons granulated garlic, 2 teaspoons toasted sesame seeds, 1½ teaspoons poppy seeds,** and **½ teaspoon kosher salt** in cup. Spray popcorn with canola nonstick spray; sprinkle popcorn with seasoning mix. Per serving: 2 cups

## Curried popcorn with dried cherries

**Prep 3 min Cook 30 sec Serves 4**

Stir together **4 teaspoons canola oil** and **2½ teaspoons curry powder** in microwavable cup. Microwave on High until fragrant, about 30 seconds. Drizzle **8 cups popcorn** with curry oil, tossing until coated evenly. Sprinkle with **¼ cup chopped dried tart cherries** and **3 tablespoons sunflower seeds.** Per serving: 2 cups

## Parmesan popcorn with lemon and thyme

## Everything-bagel popcorn

## Curried popcorn with dried cherries

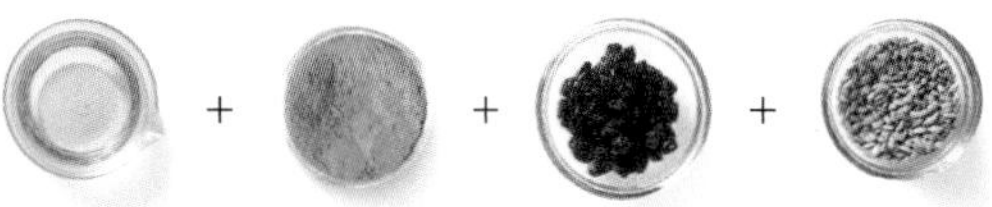

START WITH THE BASE

## Instant Pot® low-fat yogurt

**Prep 5 min Cook 3–8 hrs Serves 4**

- **4 cups low-fat (1%) milk**
- **1 cup water**
- **6 teaspoons plain low-fat yogurt with active cultures**

1. Pour milk into 4- to 8-ounce glass jars. Pour water into Instant Pot and put metal rack in pot. Place jars on rack. Lock lid, making sure vent is closed. Press Steam and select High Pressure; set cooking time for 1 minute. When time is up, press Cancel to turn off pot. Allow pressure to naturally release.
2. Remove lid and place jars on work surface. Let milk cool to 115°F. Stir in 1½ teaspoons yogurt for each cup of milk. Return jars to Instant Pot. Lock lid, making sure vent is closed. Press Yogurt and set cooking time for 3 hours for very mild yogurt or up to 8 hours for mildly tangy yogurt.
3. When time is up, remove lid. Cover jars and refrigerate up to 2 weeks. Yogurt will continue to thicken upon standing. Per serving: 1 cup

SOME YOGURT SNACKS WE LOVE

## Cucumber-scallion raita dip with veggies

**Prep 10 min Cook 0 min Serves 2**

Mix together **⅔ cup plain low-fat yogurt, 1 shredded Persian (mini) cucumber, 2 small sliced scallions, 2 teaspoons lemon juice, ¼ teaspoon ground cumin,** and **salt and pepper** to taste in bowl. Serve with veggies like **halved baby carrot sticks, radishes, small celery stalks with leaves,** and **Belgian endive leaves.** Per serving: generous ½ cup raita

## Caprese yogurt treats

**Prep 5 min Cook 0 min Serves 2**

Divide **1 cup plain low-fat yogurt** between 2 dessert bowls or glass cups. Top evenly with **½ cup chopped cherry tomatoes, 6 sliced basil leaves,** and **2 teaspoons pine nuts.** Drizzle evenly with **1 teaspoon extra-virgin olive oil** and sprinkle with **few pinches coarse sea salt and black pepper.** Per serving: 1 bowl

## Yogurt-berry snacks

**Prep 2 min Cook 0 min Serves 2**

Stir together **1 cup plain low-fat yogurt, 1 tablespoon honey,** and **1 teaspoon grated orange zest** in bowl. Divide evenly between 2 dessert bowls or mason jars. Top each with **½ cup mixed fresh berries** and **2 tablespoons low-fat granola.** Per serving: 1 bowl

Cucumber-scallion raita dip with veggies

Caprese yogurt treats

Yogurt-berry snacks

# Warm tapas-style almonds

**Prep 5 min Cook 5 min Serves 4**

5 5 5

Make a double or triple batch of these easy-prep almonds to have a snack ready whenever you're craving something salty and crunchy. Dividing them into individual portions helps you stick to just one serving at a time.

**1 teaspoon olive oil**
**¾ cup blanched whole almonds**
**½ teaspoon kosher salt**
**¼ teaspoon paprika**
**Pinch cayenne, or to taste**

Heat oil in medium heavy nonstick skillet over medium-high heat. Add almonds and reduce heat to medium-low. Cook, shaking skillet occasionally, until almonds just begin to brown, about 5 minutes. Transfer almonds to serving dish. Sprinkle with salt, paprika, and cayenne; toss until coated evenly.

**Per serving** (about 17 almonds): 172 Cal, 15 g Total Fat, 1 g Sat Fat, 246 mg Sod, 5 g Total Carb, 1 g Sugar, 3 g Fib, 6 g Prot.

## Shopping tip

**Seek out almonds in a store where there is good turnover to ensure they are as fresh as possible. Purchasing them in bulk is often less expensive.**

# Chickpea-lemon bruschetta

**Prep 15 min  Cook 0 min  Serves 12**

3 2 2

Italian bruschetta are lightly toasted slices of bread that can be topped with a range of ingredients. Chickpeas, red onion, and a hit of fresh lemon star in this version. If you have other beans on hand, like small white beans, you can use them instead.

**1 (15½-ounce) can chickpeas, rinsed and drained**
**¼ cup finely chopped red onion**
**Grated zest of 1 lemon**
**1 tablespoon lemon juice**
**2 teaspoons olive oil**
**1 garlic clove, minced**
**Pinch cayenne**
**1 (8-ounce) baguette, cut on diagonal into 12 slices and lightly toasted**
**¼ teaspoon paprika, preferably smoked**
**Coarsely chopped fresh flat-leaf parsley**

**1** With fork, mash chickpeas in medium bowl. Add onion, lemon zest and juice, oil, garlic, and cayenne, stirring until mixed well.

**2** Spoon chickpea mixture onto toasts and sprinkle with paprika and parsley. Arrange on platter and serve.

**Per serving** (1 bruschetta): 111 Cal, 2 g Total Fat, 0 g Sat Fat, 203 mg Sod, 18 g Total Carb, 2 g Sugar, 3 g Fib, 4 g Prot.

## Serve with

Turn bruschetta into lunch by serving them with a crisp green salad seasoned with vinegar and a touch of salt and topped with 1 tablespoon crumbled soft goat cheese.

# Smoked salmon canapes

**Prep 12 min Cook 0 min Serves 1**

4 3 3

A bit special and very delicious, this finger-food snack is easy to prepare. Whole-grain bread is spread with cream cheese and piled with smoked salmon, dill, capers, red onion, and a touch of grated lemon zest. It's easily big-batched for sharing with friends.

- **1 slice whole-grain or whole-wheat bread**
- **1 tablespoon light cream cheese (Neufchâtel)**
- **1 ounce thinly sliced smoked salmon**
- **1 teaspoon chopped fresh dill**
- **1 teaspoon nonpareil (tiny) capers**
- **1 teaspoon finely chopped red onion**
- **1 teaspoon grated lemon zest**

**1** Lightly toast bread; remove crust.

**2** Spread warm bread with cream cheese and top with salmon. Cut into 4 triangles; sprinkle with dill, capers, onion, and lemon zest.

**Per serving** (4 salmon-topped triangles): 147 Cal, 5 g Total Fat, 2 g Sat Fat, 850 mg Sod, 16 g Total Carb, 3 g Sugar, 2 g Fib, 10 g Prot.

## Smart pointers

Top the cream cheese with thinly sliced English (seedless) cucumber for some fresh flavor and 0 additional SmartPoints®.

# Chunky guacamole-topped rice cakes

**Prep 12 min Cook 0 min Serves 4**

4 4 4

A just-ripe avocado makes the best guacamole. Gently press down on the stem end. If it gives slightly, the avocado is ripe. If you're not using a ripe one right away, store it in the crisper drawer of your fridge for up to several days.

- **1 Hass avocado, halved, pitted, and peeled**
- **1 plum tomato, chopped**
- **½ jalapeño pepper, seeded and minced**
- **2 teaspoons lime juice, or to taste**
- **¼ teaspoon salt, or to taste**
- **4 (4-inch) thin square rice cakes, such as brown rice or rice-quinoa blend**

With fork, coarsely mash avocado (leave some chunks) in medium bowl. Add tomato, jalapeño, lime juice, and salt, gently stirring to combine. Top rice cakes evenly with guacamole.

**Per serving** (1 guacamole-topped rice cake): 123 Cal, 8 g Total Fat, 1 g Sat Fat, 152 mg Sod, 13 g Total Carb, 1 g Sugar, 4 g Fib, 2 g Prot.

## Smart pointers

Sprinkle with finely diced red onion or scallion, chopped fresh cilantro, and/or additional jalapeño for 0 SmartPoints®.

# Miso hummus with veggie chips

**Prep 25 min Cook 40 min Serves 9**

3 1 1

Freshly cooked dried chickpeas make the best hummus, and in the Instant Pot® they're melt-in-your-mouth tender in just 40 minutes. We've given this hummus a delicious Asian twist with the addition of probiotic-rich miso and a hint of ginger, sesame oil, and scallions.

**½ pound dried chickpeas (about 1 cup)**
**4 cups water**
**½ teaspoon salt**
**⅓ cup white miso**
**¼ cup lemon juice**
**1 tablespoon olive oil**
**1 large garlic clove, chopped**
**1 teaspoon Asian (dark) sesame oil**
**1 teaspoon grated peeled fresh ginger**
**½ cup chopped fresh cilantro**
**2 scallions, thinly sliced**
**1 teaspoon toasted sesame seeds**
**Thinly sliced peeled red and golden beets, radishes, daikon radish, Chioggia beets, and jicama, for dipping**

**1** Combine chickpeas, water, and salt in 6-quart Instant Pot. Lock lid, making sure vent is closed. Press Pressure Cook and select High Pressure; set cooking time for 40 minutes. When time is up, press Cancel to turn off pot. Allow pressure to naturally release for 10 minutes. Move steam-release valve to Venting position to release remaining pressure. Remove lid.

**2** With slotted spoon, transfer chickpeas to food processor. Pour water from Instant Pot into glass measure. Add ½ cup bean water to food processor along with miso, lemon juice, olive oil, garlic, sesame oil, and ginger. Process until smooth, adding more bean water if mixture seems dry.

**3** Scrape hummus into serving bowl and stir in cilantro and half of scallions. Sprinkle with remaining scallions and sesame seeds. Serve with vegetable dippers.

**Per serving** (⅓ cup hummus): 126 Cal, 4 g Total Fat, 0 g Sat Fat, 316 mg Sod, 19 g Total Carb, 5 g Sugar, 4 g Fib, 6 g Prot.

# Crunchy onion rings with kefir ranch dip

**Prep 20 min  Cook 9 min  Serves 6**

6 6 6

Thanks to the air fryer, these onion rings stay crunchy outside and tender inside. Our ranch-style dip is made with kefir, a fermented milk drink that has plenty of protein plus active probiotics. Make a double batch of the dip and use to drizzle over your favorite salad.

**KEFIR DIP**

- **½ cup kefir or low-fat buttermilk**
- **6 tablespoons light mayonnaise**
- **1 garlic clove, minced**
- **3 tablespoons chopped fresh chives**
- **2 tablespoons chopped fresh flat-leaf parsley**
- **½ teaspoon rice vinegar**
- **¼ teaspoon salt**
- **⅛ teaspoon black pepper**

**ONION RINGS**

- **½ cup all-purpose flour**
- **½ cup kefir or low-fat buttermilk**
- **1 large egg**
- **¼ teaspoon cayenne**
- **½ teaspoon salt**
- **¼ teaspoon granulated garlic**
- **1¼ cups panko (Japanese) bread crumbs**
- **3 medium onions (about 1 pound), cut into ½-inch slices, separated into rings (save small inner rings for another use)**

1. To make kefir dip, whisk together all dip ingredients in small bowl until blended. Let stand to allow flavors to blend.
2. To make onion rings, spread ¼ cup flour on sheet of wax paper. Whisk together kefir, egg, remaining ¼ cup flour, cayenne, salt, and granulated garlic in medium bowl until smooth. Spread panko on separate sheet of wax paper.
3. Coat onion rings, 5 at a time, with flour. Dip coated rings into batter, letting excess batter drip off, then coat with panko. Arrange on baking sheet in single layer. Repeat to coat remaining onion rings.
4. Preheat air fryer to 360°F for 3 minutes. Lightly spray basket with nonstick spray. Place single layer of onions rings in basket. Spray rings with nonstick spray and air-fry 5 minutes. Turn rings over and spray with nonstick spray. Air-fry until crispy, 4 minutes longer. Repeat with remaining onion rings. Serve with dip.

**Per serving** (about 6 onion rings and 2 tablespoons dip): 214 Cal, 6 g Total Fat, 1 g Sat Fat, 652 mg Sod, 31 g Total Carb, 6 g Sugar, 2 g Fib, 7 g Prot.

## Shopping tip

Almost any type of onion is good for onion rings, including white, yellow, and sweet onions like Vidalia, Maui, Walla Walla, or Texas Sweet. Choose onions that are very hard and firm, with no soft spots.

# Homemade tater tots

**Prep 25 min   Cook 30 min   Serves 4**

Use your air fryer to make crispy, irresistibly delicious potato nuggets. We like them with spicy sriracha ketchup, available at some grocery stores. Or make your own by combining a scant ¼ cup ketchup with 2 teaspoons sriracha.

- **2 pounds Yukon Gold potatoes (4 large), peeled**
- **¼ cup thinly sliced scallions (about 2 scallions)**
- **1 tablespoon cornstarch**
- **¾ teaspoon salt**
- **¼ teaspoon black pepper**
- **¼ cup sriracha ketchup or plain ketchup, for serving**

**1** Put potatoes in large saucepan and add enough salted water to cover; bring to boil. Reduce heat and simmer just until potatoes are barely tender in center when pierced, about 12 minutes (don't overcook). Drain and rinse under cold running water. Let cool.

**2** Shred potatoes on large holes of box grater. Transfer to large bowl; add scallions. Sprinkle with cornstarch, salt, and pepper and gently toss until combined.

**3** Measure out potato mixture by rounded tablespoonfuls; form into small log shapes, about 1½ inches long and 1 inch wide. Arrange on baking sheet in single layer.

**4** Preheat air fryer to 360°F for 3 minutes. Lightly spray basket with nonstick spray. Place single layer of tater tots in basket. Spray with nonstick spray and air-fry 10 minutes. Turn tots over and spray with nonstick spray. Air-fry until crispy, 5 minutes longer. Cover to keep warm or pop into a 200°F oven while air-frying the remaining tots. Serve with ketchup.

**Per serving** (8 tater tots and 1 tablespoon ketchup): 183 Cal, 0 g Total Fat, 0 g Sat Fat, 663 mg Sod, 42 g Total Carb, 6 g Sugar, 6 g Fib, 4 g Prot.

# Pepperoni pizza snacks

**Prep 30 min  Cook 23 min  Serves 12**

This snack has all the tempting flavor of a tasty pizza but without a lot of fuss. In place of pizza dough, we use wonton wrappers, which cook up crisp and help keep SmartPoints® low. Turkey pepperoni is a great lower-fat alternative to traditional pork-based pepperoni.

- **1 teaspoon olive oil**
- **5 ounces cremini mushrooms, stems trimmed and caps thinly sliced**
- **1 garlic clove, minced**
- **1 (14½-ounce) can diced tomatoes**
- **½ teaspoon dried oregano**
- **¼ teaspoon salt**
- **¼ teaspoon black pepper**
- **12 wonton wrappers**
- **6 tablespoons shredded part-skim mozzarella**
- **12 thin slices turkey pepperoni (about 1 ounce)**

**Fresh chopped oregano, for garnish (optional)**

**1** Place rack in middle of oven and preheat to 425°F.

**2** Heat oil in medium skillet set over medium-high heat. Add mushrooms and cook, stirring frequently, until liquid is evaporated and mushrooms are golden, about 7 minutes. Transfer mushrooms to small bowl and set aside.

**3** Add garlic to skillet and cook, stirring, until fragrant, about 30 seconds. Add tomatoes, dried oregano, salt, and pepper. Reduce heat to medium and cook, stirring occasionally, until sauce is slightly thickened, about 4 minutes.

**4** Coat 12-cup muffin pan with nonstick spray. Place one wonton wrapper in each cup, pressing gently to line bottoms and sides of cups. Place rounded ½ tablespoon mushrooms in each wonton liner; top each with 1½ tablespoons tomato sauce. Bake 4 minutes. Sprinkle each with ½ tablespoon mozzarella and top with 1 slice pepperoni. Bake until cheese is melted, about 5 minutes longer. Garnish with fresh oregano, if desired.

**Per serving** (1 pizza snack): 49 Cal, 1 g Total Fat, 0 g Sat Fat, 204 mg Sod, 7 g Total Carb, 1 g Sugar, 1 g Fib, 3 g Prot.

## Prep ahead

The mushrooms, as well as the tomato sauce, can be cooked up to a day ahead and refrigerated.

# Blue corn nachos

**Prep 10 min Cook 20 min Serves 8**

4 3 3

You get plenty of gooey, melty cheese on these nachos, plus a bounty of fresh tomatoes, scallions, jalapeño pepper, and fresh cilantro. Be sure to arrange the chips in a single layer in the baking dish so there's plenty of surface area for the toppings.

- **36 baked blue corn tortilla chips**
- **1 (15½-ounce) can no-salt-added pinto beans, rinsed and drained**
- **2 plum tomatoes, chopped**
- **2 scallions, thinly sliced**
- **1 jalapeño pepper, seeded and minced**
- **1 cup shredded reduced-fat Monterey Jack**
- **¼ cup chopped fresh cilantro**

**1** Preheat oven to 400°F. Spray 9 x 13-inch baking dish with nonstick spray.

**2** Arrange 24 tortilla chips in prepared baking dish in single layer. Top with beans, tomatoes, scallions, and jalapeño. Crush remaining 12 tortilla chips and sprinkle on top. Sprinkle evenly with Monterey Jack.

**3** Bake until heated through and cheese is melted, about 20 minutes. Sprinkle with cilantro.

**Per serving** (⅛ of nachos): 139 Cal, 4 g Total Fat, 2 g Sat Fat, 177 mg Sod, 18 g Total Carb, 1 g Sugar, 4 g Fib, 8 g Prot.

## Serving idea

Turn leftovers into chilaquiles by adding a beaten egg or two and cooking it in a skillet.

# Fruit-and-grain snack bars

**Prep 12 min Cook 20 min Serves 32**

3 3 3

These bars are packed with good-for-you ingredients. Dried fruit, sunflower seeds, nuts, and whole grains ensure that one small flavor-rich bar satisfies.

- **1½ cups mixed dried fruit, such as apricots, cranberries, and raisins**
- **1 cup quick-cooking or old-fashioned (rolled) oats**
- **½ cup unsalted sunflower seeds**
- **½ cup toasted wheat germ**
- **½ cup chopped pecans or walnuts**
- **½ cup nonfat dry milk powder**
- **¼ cup white whole-wheat flour**
- **1 teaspoon cinnamon**
- **½ teaspoon salt**
- **1 ripe banana, cut into chunks**
- **2 large eggs**
- **⅓ cup pure maple syrup**
- **1 teaspoon vanilla extract**

**1** Preheat oven to 350°F. Spray 9 x 13-inch baking pan with nonstick spray.

**2** Combine dried fruit, oats, sunflower seeds, wheat germ, pecans, dry milk, flour, cinnamon, and salt in food processor; pulse until dried fruit is finely chopped but not pureed. Add banana, eggs, maple syrup, and vanilla; pulse just until combined.

**3** Transfer fruit mixture to prepared pan. With damp fingertips, press down to form even layer. Bake until bars are golden and firm to the touch, about 20 minutes. Let cool completely in pan on wire rack. Cut into 32 bars.

**Per serving** (1 bar): 82 Cal, 3 g Total Fat, 0 g Sat Fat, 62 mg Sod, 13 g Total Carb, 8 g Sugar, 2 g Fib, 3 g Prot.

## Prep ahead

Covered, the bars keep in the fridge or at cool room temperature up to 5 days or can be frozen up to 4 months.

**Sweet potato lasagna with turkey and sage, page 92**

# Recipes by SmartPoints® value

Green

## 6 SmartPoints value



## 7 SmartPoints value



## 8 SmartPoints value



## 9 SmartPoints value



## 10 SmartPoints value



## 11 SmartPoints value



## 12 SmartPoints value

## 0 SmartPoints value



## 1 SmartPoints value

## 2 SmartPoints value



## 3 SmartPoints value



## 4 SmartPoints value



## 5 SmartPoints value



## 6 SmartPoints value

## 7 SmartPoints value



## 8 SmartPoints value



## 9 SmartPoints value



## 12 SmartPoints value

## 0 SmartPoints value



## 1 SmartPoints value



## 2 SmartPoints value

## 3 SmartPoints value



## 4 SmartPoints value



## 5 SmartPoints value



## 6 SmartPoints value



## 7 SmartPoints value



## 8 SmartPoints value



## 9 SmartPoints value

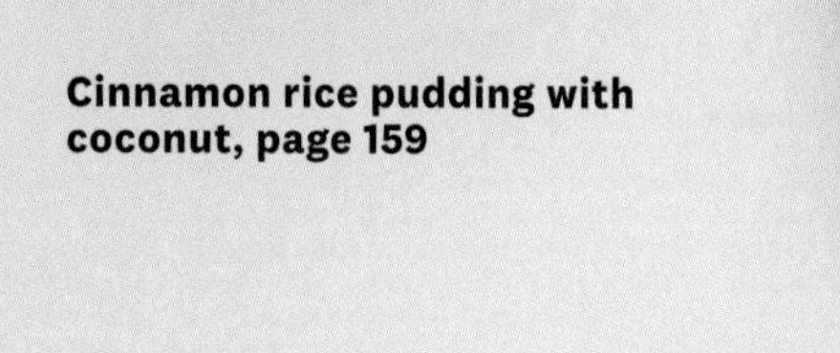

**Cinnamon rice pudding with coconut, page 159**

# Index

## C

## D



## E

## I



## J



## K



## L

## P

## T



## V